VOLUME
11

Originally published in the United Kingdom in weekly parts **COMBAT & SURVIVAL** is a study of the armed forces at work. It shows the skills taught to soldiers and the way in which military units operate. It examines the weapons and equipment used by different armies; and, by looking at recruit training and exercises, **COMBAT & SURVIVAL** demonstrates how the armed forces develop individual responsibility, leadership and initiative.

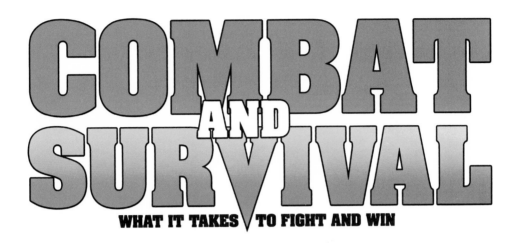

WHAT IT TAKES TO FIGHT AND WIN

VOLUME
11

H. S. STUTTMAN, INC. *publishers*   Westport, Connecticut 06889

Contents
Volume 11

Combat Skills	Infantry Skills No. 13: Infantry Minelaying	**605**
	Infantry Skills No. 14: Digging In	**611**
	Infantry Skills No. 15: Deception	**617**

Battle Fitness Program	No. 7: Warming Up	**622**
	No. 8: Aerobic Exercise	**624**
	No. 9: Training Your Heart	**626**

Weapons and Equipment Guide	No. 30: RPG-7: Rocket from Russia	**628**
	No. 31: M113: Crashing into Action	**634**
	No. 32: T-54/55: Desert Warrior	**640**

Survival	Trapping Animals for Food	**646**
	Fishing for Food	**650**
	Preserving Food	**654**

Fighting Fit	Combat Infantryman Week 11: First Battle Camp	**658**
	Combat Infantryman Weeks 12-15: The Bunker Buster	**662**

Combat Reports	Rhodesia: Alouette Raid Part 1	**610**
	Rhodesia: Alouette Raid Part 2	**616**
	Vietnam: Combat Air Controller	**661**

Published by H. S. STUTTMAN INC.
Westport, Connecticut 06889
© Aerospace Publishing 1991
ISBN 0-87475-560-3

INFANTRY MINELAYING

5 POINTS FOR LAYING A PROTECTIVE MINEFIELD

Protective minefields are laid by individual units, not by the Royal Engineers, who will definitely have better things to do. Note:

1. This type of minefield is designed to stop Sabre tanks only, so you should site your anti-tank weapons to cope with mine rollers and ploughs.
2. Protective fields are usually only one panel in depth: that is, five rows of the ancient Mk 7 or three rows of the single-impulse bar mines. This will stop about 70 per cent of Sabre tanks.
3. For planning purposes, 25 men can lay 150 mines on the surface per hour.
4. Mines are heavy; you can only get 275 Mk 7 mines on a four-ton truck.
5. Mines are classified as ammunition and are demanded in the normal way, but minefield marking stores come from the Engineers.

Minelaying is primarily the business of the engineers on the battlefield — but there are never enough engineers to go round. So the infantry have had to learn to look after themselves in many situations. This is mainly the task of the Assault Pioneer Platoon, who are trained in basic minelaying skills, but another way of getting round the problem of the engineer shortage is for engineer NCOs to supervise parties of infantrymen or, indeed, of any type of soldier whom they can use as a directed labour force.

Anti-tank mines

There are two basic types of mine: the anti-tank mine and the anti-personnel mine. An anti-tank mine is designed to stop a tank or other armoured vehicle so that, if it is not destroyed by the mine, it immediately becomes vulnerable to manned weapons. There are four types of anti-tank mine in service with the British Army: the old Mk 7 mine, of which there are still large stockpiles; the non-metallic L3A1 mine; the L9A1 bar mine; and the L14A1 off-route mine.

The Mk 7 mine can be fitted with a double impulse or a tilt fuse and the bar mine can be fitted with single impulse, double impulse or anti-disturbance fuses. The double impulse fuse is designed to counter the mine-clearing roller. It allows the roller to create the first impulse, which it ignores, and then detonates when the tank track rolls over the mine.

Mining tarmac roads is always difficult unless there is a conveniently-placed culvert or drain. The off-route mine, as the name suggests, is placed in the verge on the side of the road and fires a self-forging fragment through the side armour of any tank breaking the circuit wire stretched across the road.

HAND MINELAYING DRILL 'C'

All protective minefields of single-impulse mines laid by hand use a set drill known as drill 'C'. It is a fast, efficient and safe way to lay mines in the absence of engineer help. In view of the enemy armour threat and his disturbing habit of driving right onto your defensive position, it is a skill vital to your survival. The drill is carried out by one officer and 25 men, divided into five parties as follows:

1 The setting-out party.
2 The fencing party.
3 The positioning party.
4 The digging party.
5 Camouflage and arming party.

Obviously, if the mines are to be surface-laid the digging party can be deleted.

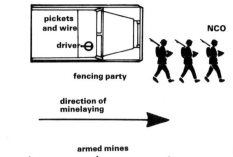

pickets and wire

driver

NCO

fencing party

direction of enemy

Fencing party
This consists of one NCO, two soldiers and a vehicle and driver to carry pickets, wire and minefield triangles. Their tasks are to pace out 15m between pickets and hammer in a picket and attach an ankle wire and a waist wire. They should also attach a line sign at least every 50m. Ideally they should use existing fences as far as possible and simply mark them up.

direction of minelaying →

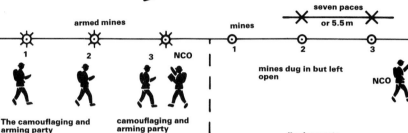

armed mines

1   2   3   NCO

mines

1   2   3

seven paces or 5.5m

NCO

enemy

home s

mines dug in but left open

NCO

positioning party

The camouflaging and arming party
This is controlled by the minefield-laying party 2IC, usually a platoon sergeant. He controls the three soldiers in the party. A driver and Land Rover are used to carry stores and personal weapons. If the mines are surface-laid, then there would be no digging party and an extra two in the arming party. The NCO directs the three soldiers to their first three mines in the row and supervises the arming and camouflaging of the AT mines and the laying of the AP mines. The NCO is also responsible for the arming of AP mines, which is done last so that no-one has to walk past an armed mine. The NCO is also responsible for collecting all signs of mining, such as fuse clips, pins and

camouflaging and arming party

driver

wrapping paper. Each man stays at his mine until he is told to move and the three soldiers work in unison. When they have finished, soldier 1 moves first, round the back of 2 and 3, to the first mine of the next triplet, and then 2 moves back, followed by 3. This is very carefully controlled by the NCO so that there is no chance of walking over an armed mine.

digging party

The digging party
This consists of one NCO and seven soldiers with digging tools: they follow up the positioning party. The NCO allots a mine to be buried by each soldier and inspects his work to ensure that the hole is deep enough for the mine. The mines are dug in but left exposed. Once a

soldier has dug in his mine to the satisfaction of the NCO, he moves along the home side to the next mine in the row and continues the process. Any AP mines are left on top of the AT mine ready for the arming and camouflaging party.

positioning soldier
positioning soldier 2

mi

Positioning party
This consists of four soldiers, including th driver of the vehicle containing the mine commanded by an N The NCO lines up th vehicle with the line markers marking the setting-out line. The vehicle follows this about two metres aw the home side. Whe laying commences, soldier in the rear of vehicle passes a mir one of the two mine positioning soldiers also keeps a record many mines he issu Anti-personnel mine issued at the same t The mines are laid se

direction of laying →

The tilt fuse is activated either by the direct pressure of a vehicle track or wheel or by the belly of the vehicle striking and fracturing the tilt fuse mast. This means that the mine can attack the full width of the vehicle.

The anti-disturbance fuse is designed primarily to counteract a mine-clearing plough. In other words, it can be knocked about a bit by the plough, but should not explode until several tons of pressure has been exerted upon it.

Anti-personnel mines contain a small explosive charge and are set off by a weight of about four kilograms or more – in other words, the pressure of a man's foot. They are designed to wound or possibly kill. There are two main types; one relies on blast and the other on fragmentation.

Lethal fragments

The blast type is small, weighing as little as 100g, contains a small amount of explosive, and is designed to injure the leg or foot. The fragmentation type is either a composite or jumping mine.

Although mines can be laid with double impulse and metallic influence fuses, your main weapons against the roller and the mine plough are your anti-tank weapons. These tanks must be your priority targets: but not this one, as this is a US M60 Roller tank.

The setting-out party should select a feature off the map to relate the start point to. It is essential to pick a prominent feature that will still be there after intensive shelling, such as the corner of a large wood.

It either throws a canister into the air, where it explodes and scatters lethal fragments over a wide area; or it is a directional mine such as the M18A1 Claymore, now no longer in British service. Jumping mines are not in British service either, though they are used by NATO and Warsaw Pact armies. The two types of blast mine in service with the British Army are the non-metallic C3 mine ('Elsie') and the L10A2 Ranger mine.

The British bar mine is particularly effective because of its shape. It is 1.2 metres long and only 108 mm wide and 81 mm high, which means there is statistically more chance of a tank running over it if it is placed at 90° to the expected direction of the enemy's approach than if it were circular, like the Mk 7 or the non-metallic LA3A1 mine. It was a British 'first', and is still the only oblong mine in wide service in the world today.

Horizontal fire

The off-route mine also has special features. It is used to cover a wider frontage than the normal anti-tank mine and, as its name implies, it is designed to be placed off to one side of a track. It is usually set to fire horizontally at the passing target vehicle, which sets the mine off when it ruptures a breakwire; this can be laid out to a length of about 80 metres in its path.

The Ranger mine system also deserves more detailed description. The mine projector can be mounted on the FV 432 or the Stalwart as well as on the standard Bedford 4-tonne truck, and is designed to lay anti-personnel mines by scattering them over a selected area some distance away from the vehicle.

Mixed minefield

The idea is to project them into an anti-tank minefield, thus creating a mixed minefield which is obviously much more difficult to clear, particularly by hand. The rate of fire can be varied to suit the vehicle's speed and the density of minefield required. The maximum rate of fire is three barrels, each of 18 mines, per second. The range can vary from 120 metres with a lateral spread of up to 30 metres, down to 40 metres with a lateral spread of up to 15 metres.

As an infantryman you could be required to lay various types of minefield. The first is the **tactical minefield**, which is an integral part of the commander's tactical plan for winning the battle. The aim may be to break up the enemy's advance or to

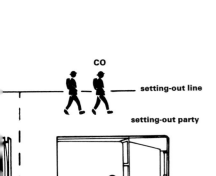

CO — setting-out line

setting-out party

Setting out party
This consists of the officer in charge of the operation and one soldier with a vehicle to carry stores. Their job is to select a marker and plot its position very carefully on the minefield record. They then set out pickets marking the centre of the mine rows and relate these to the marker on the mine map. The pickets marking the rows will usually be driven flush with the ground, and the rows will usually be laid in an irregular pattern on set bearings and distances marked and recorded by the setting-out party. They also record the number and type of mines laid when laying is complete.

apart: the NCO this distance out ops, indicating to the positioning s to place an anti-ine at his heels. AP are simply piled on the AT mine. The ehicle is driven parallel to the line, controlled by O.

The minefield must be very carefully mapped using pacing and compass bearings of all the changes in direction that make up the irregular outer edge of the minefield. The commander would use the prismatic compass for this task.

CURRENT BRITISH ANTI-TANK MINES

The off-route mine
This fires a horizontal shaped charge from the side of a road at anything that drives over and cuts the break wire sensor. This mine is due to be replaced by the LAW 80 system.

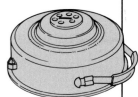

The Mk 7 mine
The mine weighs around 13.6 kg, of which 9 kg is explosive. It is armed by removing the mine cap with a spanner, removing the safety clip from the cylindrical fuse and replacing it the other way up before screwing the cap back on. Special mine cap spanners are required for the job.

The bar mine
This is a modern plastic rectangular mine containing 8.4 kg of explosive. It has an integral pressure fuse and is armed by removing the safety pin and turning the arming switch on the side from safe to armed.

The bar mine can now be fitted with a range of add-on fuses, which will normally only be laid by the Engineers. These new-generation fuses include an anti-disturbance fuse and full-width attack fuses.

TACTICAL MINEFIELDS

POINT AND INTERDICTION MINEFIELDS

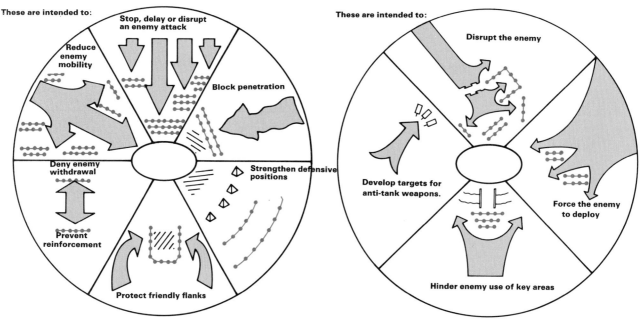

These are intended to:
Stop, delay or disrupt an enemy attack
Reduce enemy mobility
Block penetration
Strengthen defensive positions
Deny enemy withdrawal
Prevent reinforcement
Protect friendly flanks

These are intended to:
Disrupt the enemy
Develop targets for anti-tank weapons.
Force the enemy to deploy
Hinder enemy use of key areas

In addition to protective minefields, the US Army have two further classifications of minefields that carry out the same task as Royal Engineer-laid tactical minefields. A tactical minefield is part of the overall barrier plan where there is an imminent threat of enemy ground attack. It is designed to fulfil the purposes outlined above.

These are usually laid within range of division-level weapons. Point minefields are of irregular size and shape, and can vary in composition, from a single group of mines, or what the British Army would term a nuisance cluster, to a series of mined areas along major lines of communication or approach routes. Both conventional and scatterable mines can be used. The aim is to add effect to natural and man-made obstacles.

delay him to give the anti-tank weapons better targets to shoot at. They will form a vital part of the defensive layout and are usually laid by engineers using mechanical means, but you could be asked to assist them.

But you are much more likely to be involved in the laying of a **protective minefield**. These are for the close protection of a defensive position or installation, and their laying is the responsibility of all arms. They are much more likely to be laid by hand.

Receiving the enemy

The third type of minefield is the **nuisance minefield**. These can be laid either by engineers or assault pioneers, and are usually laid on the verges of roads or where you think the enemy may halt, or you could use them to create an irregular outer edge to a tactical minefield.

The last category of minefield is the **phoney minefield**. It is marked as a minefield and wired off as one, and to all intents and purposes looks like one – except there are no mines! You can use them as a minefield gap for your own forces where necessary, or just to delay the enemy. It will take him some

time to discover that it's a fake.

There are two types of minefield pattern: strips or rows. A mine strip consists of two parallel rows of mines laid simultaneously six metres apart. This is an acceptable minefield pattern and may be used by some NATO countries, but it is not used by the British Army. Current British mine-laying drills, known as Drill C and Drill D, are for laying mine clusters in single rows. Drill C is for single-mine or mixed clusters; Drill D is for laying Mk 7 anti-tank mines with tilt fuses. You will need one officer and 24 men to carry out Drill C, while Drill D requires one more man.

Drill C is based on use of the Standard Mk 7 anti-tank mine but it may be used for other anti-tank (except the Mk 7 with the tilt fuse) or anti-personnel mines. The drill requires a fencing party of one NCO, two soldiers and a driver, whose job it is to delineate the minefield. Then a setting-out party of one NCO, two soldiers and a driver will set out pickets to indicate the centre lines of rows, plant finishing-row markers, record the numbers and types of mines, and record each lane entrance by means of a landmark and a bearing.

Clusters, rows and panels

Protective minefields are made up of one panel containing four or five rows of mine clusters. Tactical minefields may be made up of several panels. The basic unit of the minefield row is the cluster, which can be any of the following:

1 One single anti-tank mine.
2 One anti-tank mine surrounded by not more than four anti-personnel mines within a two-pace semicircle.
3 One single anti-personnel mine.
4 A semicircle of not more than four anti-personnel mines on or round a central anti-personnel mine.

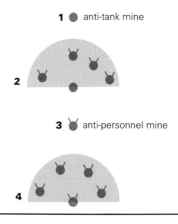

1 ● anti-tank mine

2

3 anti-personnel mine

4

A TYPICAL THREE-ROW PROTECTIVE MINEFIELD WITH SAFETY DISTANCES

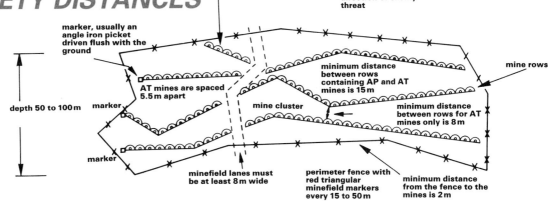

Note
The irregular outer edges are an optional extra designed to confuse the enemy as to the size, shape and laying pattern of the minefield. They are usually laid as a short row of up to eight clusters. The ends of each row in the panel are marked with a row marker which is related to the landmark on the minefield map. Mine rows should, where possible, follow the edges of the tracks and fence lines to aid camouflage.

irregular outer edge

direction of enemy threat

marker, usually an angle iron picket driven flush with the ground

mine rows

minimum distance between rows containing AP and AT mines is 15 m

AT mines are spaced 5.5 m apart

mine cluster

minimum distance between rows for AT mines only is 8 m

depth 50 to 100 m

marker

marker

minefield lanes must be at least 8 m wide

perimeter fence with red triangular minefield markers every 15 to 50 m

minimum distance from the fence to the mines is 2 m

Then comes the positioning party, consisting of one NCO and four soldiers, including a driver, who simply lay the mine or the ground 5.5 metres apart as indicated by the NCO. Then the digging party (one NCO and seven men) dig the mines into the ground, but leave them exposed. Last come the camouflage and arming party (one NCO, three soldiers and a driver). Their job must be carefully controlled since, once the mines are armed, they must not stray back into the 'live' part of the minefield – particularly if anti-personnel mines have

been added.

Drill C is a slow and painstaking process, but it is worth all the effort. If you are sitting in a defensive position you will feel a great deal more secure with a minefield in front of you, and seeing enemy tanks erupt in front of your eyes does great things for morale.

Whatever type of minefield you construct, there are two golden rules. First, the effectiveness of minefields depends largely on the element of surprise. An unexpected obstacle does more to disorganise an attack than one whose position and characteristics are

known in advance. So make every effort to conceal the minefield by putting it in a valley or in scrubland or, if this is not possible, conceal the location of mine rows and individual mines as far as possible.

Secondly, the value of a minefield, as of any other obstacle, depends largely upon the degree to which fire can be brought to bear on the enemy. It is only by dominating a minefield and preventing interference with it that you can rely on it as an obstacle. So cover all minefields by fire – preferably by direct fire.

MINEFIELD LANES

diagram shows the layout of a tion of a protective minefield, ding a minefield lane and a drawal route. Note the wing points.

ft ground
i-tank mines must be dug in in n ground, otherwise the tank shes the mine down and fails to the mine. In soft ground, place w stones in the bottom of the e to provide a firm base for the ne to actuate the pressure plate. e turf covering the mine should left slightly proud of the ground the same reason.

nstruction route
en laying your protective efield, remember it may be cessary to leave a gap so that nes can be brought forward from mine dump to the minelaying ns. These construction routes l have to be closed when the d is complete.

aters
ads blocked by cratering must o be mined to prevent the emy driving round the craters or ng to fill them in. Road blocks uld be treated in a similar hion.

ithdrawal routes
make the best of your long-nge anti-tank weapons such as LAN, you may well have to site em out to the flank and forward your main defensive position. itable gaps will have to be left d the withdrawal practised so at everyone knows the thdrawal route and can find it in e dark.

Observation and fire
A minefield must be covered by fire to be an effective obstacle. The Soviets specialise in assault minefield breaching.

Nuisance minefields
Although these are not marked they should be guarded until all friendly forces are clear of the area. Building and track junctions are just the places for nuisance clusters.

Closing lanes
Lanes can be closed by additional mining when an attack is imminent. All mines must be recorded on the minefield record.

Minefield lanes
Always leave a lane through your own protective field for use by your own patrols. These must be very carefully planned and recce'd and all patrol commanders must be very carefully briefed. You can mark the lane on your side, but any marking you do on the enemy side needs to be very unobtrusive.

Camouflage and concealment
Minefields should as far as possible be sited to achieve maximum surprise. Use dead ground or, if this is not possible, disguise the mine rows themselves in hedges or standing crops, ploughed fields or other disturbed ground.

Reporting
Before you can start, you need to make the following reports by radio, usually to your HQ:
1 An 'intention to lay' report
2 A 'minefield siting' report
3 A 'start of laying' report
4 A 'completion of laying' report

Booby traps
Booby traps and anti-lifting devices can only be used when authorised. Their position and type must be carefully noted on the minefield record which, when completed, is classified secret and is held by the engineers in the formation HQ in case the minefield needs to be lifted.

Fences
On the enemy side a single strand of knee high wire is used. On the home side this is double strand at waist and ankle height. Maximum use should be made of existing fences.

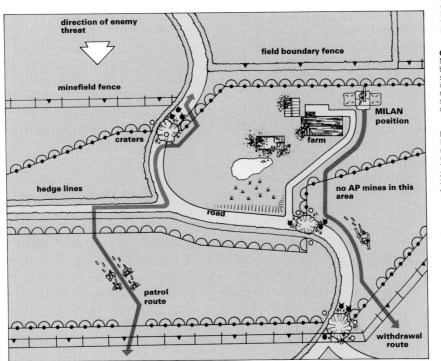

direction of enemy threat

field boundary fence

minefield fence

MILAN position

craters

farm

construction route

no AP mines in this area

hedge lines

road

patrol route

withdrawal route

Combat Report
Rhodesia:
Alouette Raid Part 1

A technician on an Alouette III squadron in the Rhodesian Air Force describes a mission to flush out terrorists from a training camp over the border.

The phone woke me at 02.15 a.m. I groped wearily for the receiver and managed to get it to my ear. "Salisbury 329427."

"Morning, Joe. Call-out. Transport is on its way."

"OK, boss. See you later."

As my brain cleared of sleep, I wondered what the buzz was. The timing of the call-out was nothing new. If you gather a number of blokes together in the ops room and give them a briefing on a forthcoming operation, then no matter how security-conscious they are, word has a way of getting out; and, once out, it travels fast, maybe to the wrong ears.

So the plan was to brief the squadron commander, who then had the job of ensuring that all the relevant personnel mustered at the squadron in the early hours of the morning on which the operation was to take place. By the time the rest of the camp arrived at work, the squadron was already airborne with nobody any the wiser.

A rush of adrenalin

I waited on the roadside for the transport. It was a warm African summer night with the rains due any time now. I was the last to be picked up and was deposited along with the rest of the fellows at the squadron. We ambled in through the main entrance and sought out the boss, who directed us to the ops room.

"Right, you buggers. We're going external. We have picked up intelligence on a terr training camp across the eastern border. Once across, it's about 20 minutes' flying time to the target. We'll be refuelling en route, by which time our reconnaissance aircraft will have confirmed the target or not, as the case may be.

"If the op is on, the camp will be hit first by the Hunters, which will hopefully soften them up a bit. We will go in with three C-ships and nine T-ships. We'll be backing up the paras, who will be dropping from two Daks. The object of the exercise is to inflict maximum damage to the terrs and their camp. The T-ships will ferry in

Helicopters throw up an incredible amount of grit taking off or landing in the dry southern African climate and it was a nightmare trying to keep the 20-mm cannon in good working order.

members of specialist units, while the C-ships will maintain top cover. The T-ships will remain on station to fly out any casevacs and also to ferry paras and their equipment to the Daks, which will be on the ground at a landing strip close by, which will have been taken earlier by the "browns."

He went on at some length, designating call signs for all the units involved, and then asked for any questions, which took up a bit more time. This was my first 'external', and I'd already had an early rush of adrenalin. When the briefing had finished, the crews dispersed: the pilots to find maps and work out fuel requirements and get met reports etc, while the techs, myself included, inspected the aircraft, making sure that they were in tip-top condition and paying special attention to the gunfits, as we would be the ones operating them later that day.

In this operation, one C-ship was to carry the operation co-ordinator; another one would carry his deputy, in case of either C-ship being forced down; and the third C-ship would be purely a gunship. I was to be the tech on second C-ship.

After ensuring that the chopper was mechanically sound, I turned my attention to the cannon. It had already been cleaned by the previous tech but, even so, I went over it again. One of the problems we encountered was the hot, dry, dusty climate of the African bush: the gritty particles of dust got everywhere and stuck to everything, especially if it was covered with a layer of oil. And, as you can imagine, a helicopter taking off or landing in the bush stirred up an awful lot of dust which in turn found its way into the cannon's mechanism.

I checked our equipment

It was a problem that had never been successfully solved, and my way around it was to clean the breech with petrol or de-greaser and leave it to dry until we were airborne en route for the target, during which time I would oil the breech. This method held up fine, until we landed for fuel during the contact, but it was the best that I could come up with. My next task was to prepare the ammo belt to my own satisfaction; my own preference was to alternate ball and HE rounds.

After feeding the ammo belt into the bin and stowing the spare barrel (in case of overheating), I checked that our personal survival equipment was close to hand, then towed the chopper outside to join the queue at the fuel dispenser. By this time it was about

Our Alouette III helicopters were tasked with providing fire support and landing ground troops to store the guerrilla base over the border.

04.00, and we sat waiting for the first glimmer of light on the horizon, which would be the signal for the off.

The operation was "go"

A short while later we were airborne, heading eastwards in three echelons of four aircraft each, making for our refuelling point at Mgvene, where we would get the "go" or "no-go" and pick up the "browns" (paras). I used the time airborne to check out the cannon's range of movement, that the electrical connections were made, that I had a screwdriver within easy reach in case of a runaway gun, and a few other minor time-absorbing tasks. Then I sat back to enjoy the sight of the three lines of choppers framed against the backdrop of the sun rising over the Eastern Highlands, wishing once again that I had remembered to bring my camera. We landed at the refuelling stop, where the pilots went into their final huddle and the rest of us pumped the right amount of Avtur into the helicopter fuel tanks.

The word was that the operation was "go". The T-ships took on their complement of four troops each, while we picked up the two C-ship commanders. We took off again and, keeping close to the contours of the Eastern Highlands, we crossed the border a short time later. Keeping 15 metres above ground level and being very wary of the helicopter's old enemy, power lines and telephone cables, we pushed on towards the target. This was when the adrenalin really started to flow.

Cessna 337 Lynxes worked alongside the Alouette helicopters, providing Rhodesian soldiers with accurately-delivered fire support in their anti-terrorist missions.

DIGGING IN

You could be forgiven for believing that the design of a trench is one military question that should have been settled years ago. However, weapons and tactics are always changing, and the best way for the infantry to dig in remains the subject of careful thought in several *NATO* armies. One of the main problems is time; everyone agrees that you must dig deep to survive a bombardment, but on a modern mobile battlefield you won't have time to build a Maginot Line.

Success in battle depends not only on effective offensive operations, but also on holding and consolidating ground from which you can mount further offensive operations when the time is right. An effective defence also causes attrition to enemy forces, so that when you do go onto the offensive he is weaker. You already know how to construct a basic defensive position, but there is more – much more – to defence than the two- or four-man basic battle trench.

First, you need to understand how a trench helps survival. Even a little digging will provide a degree of protection against the effects of nuclear and conventional weapons, but this protection increases sharply as a trench gets deeper and overhead protection is added. Artillery shells are designed either to explode at a set height (air-burst) or upon impact with the ground. In the former case, they must explode directly above your trench to stand a good chance of getting fragments into it.

Keep your head down

Provided you have had time to construct overhead cover, you can guard against this. But even if you have not, keeping below the parapet of your trench should protect you from all shell fragments except those that explode directly or almost directly over your trench.

Shells exploding on the ground would have to be virtually a direct hit to cause you any serious damage – other than a severe shock and tempor-ary deafness. The force of an explosion follows the line of least resistance and goes upwards and outwards, leaving a surprisingly small hole in the ground.

Nevertheless, trenches can be made stronger by revetment. Its purpose is threefold: to prevent the side (or wall) of an excavation from falling in under its own weight, to prevent the wall being worn away, and to strengthen it against the effects of an enemy bombardment. A wall with a vertical slope, such as in a slit trench, will give you greater protection than if the wall is sloped, but it is more likely to collapse under its own weight. Revetment prevents this.

There are two basic types of revetment: the skin revetment, which requires some form of support, and the

OVERHEAD PROTECTION

Split hairpin (left)

The split hairpin system of interlocking corrugated iron sheeting is the easiest way of getting a defensive roof over your head. Remember that 45 cm is a minimum requirement for overhead cover.

Kip sheet (right)

This trench has overhead protection provided by the Individual Protection Kit. Pickets driven into the ground about 1 metre in front of the trench support cords attached to them by a round turn and three half-hitches. The cords stretch above the trench and will support a groundsheet with the required 45 cm of earth on top.

REVETMENT

Above and right: Revetting means supporting the sides of your trench. This is always necessary in loose or sandy soil, but even a heavy clay soil cannot be relied on to stay secure under fire. You can use wriggly tin, boards, logs or whatever is available as revetting material. Secure the material to the side of the trench by hammering stakes into the floor of the trench. Pickets may be sunk into the surrounding ground and cord tied between them and the stakes for added support.

wall revetment, which stands on its own. Examples of skin revetment are corrugated galvanised iron (CGI) sheets, timber planks, expanded metal (XPM) or manufactured substances such as FRM (Flexible Revetting Material) or GRP (Glass Reinforced Plastic). Even brushwood can be used. Whatever you use, you hold the revetting material in place by long pickets driven into the ground. The pickets are anchored by wire to short pickets or held apart by struts.

Skin revetment is made even easier if the so-called 'split hairpin' shelter sheets are used. These are prefabricated curved CGI sheets that can be used either to revet the corner of a trench or to support overhead cover. Wall revetment is usually constructed from sandbags.

In highly mobile warfare you will seldom have time for revetment, but in more static operations, particularly internal security, you should have time to do it.

There are several digging methods. The most obvious is by hand using the infantryman's companion, the Mk 1 spade, and this is often the only possible method, particularly if you need to dig in covertly.

Explosive digging

A quicker method is by using explosives. The principle of explosive digging is that a number of small charges are exploded below ground to loosen the soil, so that most of it can be dug out with shovels, without the need for pickaxes.

Do not attempt to blow the soil out

of the ground to form a crater, as this will scatter the soil over a wide area with consequent loss of concealment. Also, the sides of the trench will be weakened.

If you use charges of the correct size, a crater should not be formed. The exact size of the charge will depend on the type of soil and type of trench, but will vary between 0.75 g of Plastic Explosive (PE) for a battle trench and 0.69 kg of PE for a much larger weapon pit. Place the charges in parallel lines or concentric circles depending on the type of excavation.

The third way of digging a trench is with the help of a machine. There are several available in the British Army: the most widely used is the Light Mobile Digger (LMD). This machine is specifically designed to dig trenches;

Above: The Light Mobile Digger machine is mounted on a Bedford TM 4-4 (4×4) 8-tonne truck and digs trenches at a rate of two metres per minute (clay soil), six metres (medium soil) or nine metres (light, sandy soil).

Above: A business-end view of the Soviet BTM trencher at work: based on the massive chassis of the AT-T tractor, this can excavate up to 100 m of soil per hour even when the earth is frozen.

Left: Camouflage is adjusted on a defensive position. Large heaps of soil are an obvious giveaway that most people avoid, but not everyone remembers to regularly replace the foliage. Withered leaves in an otherwise green area are another telltale sign.

Above: Digging in on a forward slope during an exercise at Otterburn – the choice of position was dictated by the practical requirements of a live firing exercise. In wartime you would dig in on the reverse slope.

the excavating mechanism is a continuous cutting chain that lifts the soil onto a conveyor belt. It can excavate a 0.60-metres-wide trench down to a maximum depth of 1.35 metres. The LMD is held by most engineer field units and by some artillery and infantry units.

Other machines are the Light Wheeled Tractor (LWT) and the Medium Wheeled Tractor (MWT), both of which are held by divisional engineer units. You may also have excavators, which are more suitable for digging anti-tank ditches than preparing battle positions. And finally, the Combat Engineer Tractor (CET) is a tracked, armoured, amphibious vehicle specially designed for use by engineer units as an earth-moving machine and general workhorse.

There are many types of trenches. The **two-man battle trench** uses either the KIP (Kit Individual Protection) sheet or 'split hairpin' to form the basis of the shelter trench. The **four-man battle trench** has shelter bays at each end of the trench or in the middle with firebays at each end. The shelter bay or bays may also be constructed

Combat Skills

with the KIP sheet or the split hairpin. If the firebays are at each end of the trench, they can be in a line with the central shelter trench or angled at up to 1600 mils.

Then there are separate designs for **GPMG** and **MILAN trenches**, both of which are modified four-man battle trenches. A particularly important feature of the MILAN trench is that the area behind it must be cleared for five metres in an extending arc of 500 mils each side of the axis of the firing tube of the weapon. This zone must be completely clear of men, equipment and obstacles to cater for the backblast of the weapon.

Weapon pits

Emplacements may also be dug for the 81-mm mortar, for the 105-mm Light Gun and even for the FH 70 155-mm towed howitzer. Pits for self-propelled guns, tanks and 'soft skinned' vehicles may also be dug if the time is available. In most cases the effort of digging in a tank will just not be worth it: the best position for a tank is on a reverse slope, where the ground gives protection and where it is possible to move to alternative positions that give the same degree of protection. Only where this is not possible might you have to dig it in.

Digging in a tank considerably reduces its vulnerability to enemy action, whether it be direct fire, air attack or nuclear weapons. Also, the best concealment against thermal imagery is to put ground between the vehicle and the surveillance device.

Left: Tasked with intensive nightly patrolling, the fire team crashes out during the day, leaving one man on stag at all times. Note the turfs piled on top of the spoil from the trench. For safety reasons, the troops were ordered to leave their weapons on the parapet.

Below: The Light Support Weapon is a vital part of the fireteam's firepower, so the gunner needs to shoot from a properly constructed parapet. Just firing over the lip of a trench like this exposes a lot of his chest to enemy rounds. Given the volume of fire likely to be directed at your defensive position, you have to offer the smallest possible target.

SUSTAINED FIRE GPMGs

There's nothing like a plentiful supply of GPMGs in the Sustained Fire role enfilading an attack to bring the enemy to a standstill. So site them well, and with full overhead protection.

In the SF role, the GPMG's range is only limited by its ammunition: new 7.62-mm rounds are being developed with longer-burning tracer, so the very long range machine-gun shoots used in both world wars will once again be possible.

Enemy firepower will be no less effective in the Arctic, but digging a good defensive position becomes a good deal harder. Given the lack of revetting material it is fortunate that the frozen soil does not need so much shoring up. Note the shelter bay and the white camouflage net protecting the position from aerial observation.

Right: Digging in the usual (hard) way, the troops take turns working with the pick and filling the sandbags. In wartime the section's weapons should be laid down, pointing at the arcs of fire allotted to them in the defensive plan. If the enemy arrive rather sooner than expected, then you are at least half ready to meet them.

US Army teaching on trench digging is little different. The same emphasis is put on clearing fields of fire, revetment, overhead cover and camouflage, and there are different trench designs for the M60 machine-gun, the Dragon anti-tank guided missile, the 90-mm recoilless rifle and mortars and larger artillery pieces.

There is, however, one notable difference. Much more emphasis is put on fire to the oblique. This results in a design that has the shelter trench in the middle with firing bays at each end, firing out to the half front and side. You may have to rely on the trench to your left and right to look after the ground directly to your front. The advantage of this system is that you are covered from fire from the front: that is, you are defiladed by your frontal cover.

The principle is certainly sound, but if mutually supporting trenches are put out of action it could result in a blind spot. The best way to achieve cover from fire from the front is to site your trench on a reverse slope position. In that way the enemy is skylined when he comes over the top of the hill and he cannot fire at you from a distance.

There is much more to the business of trench construction than meets the eye. Field defences are a complicated art. But if you do the job well, you will win the defensive battle and then you can take the offensive when the time is right.

THE FOUR-MAN BATTLE TRENCH

To build this with shelter bays at each end, you need to deturf an area 10.4 m×2.5 m, dig a survival hole and develop it to 6 m long. It should be 75 cm wide and deep enough for the tallest man in the section to be able to stand on the trench floor with his chin at ground level. Bend four 1.8-metre CGI sheets to fit the ends of the trench and revet the sides with 1.8-metre sheets overlapping by at least 10 cm. The overhead cover is fixed using the KIP system.

Overhead protection
6×1.8-metre CGI sheets on top of a picket framework will support the necessary 45 cm of overhead protection.

Wall
This should be three sandbags high with the seams inwards. Lay them together, overlapping like bricks in a wall.

Camouflage
Blend the position into its surroundings by using spare sandbags and spoil: avoid a 'sudden bump' appearing in the landscape.

Firing positions
These show as dark holes against the landscape, so camouflage them with hessian or face veils until you need to open fire.

Combat Report
Rhodesia:
Alouette Raid Part 2

A technician on an Alouette helicopter in the Rhodesian Air Force continues his account of a cross-border raid on a guerrilla training camp.

I opened up the breech of the cannon and spread a thin layer of oil over the moving parts. I closed the breech, offered up the rounds, cocked the weapon and took the safety off, ensuring that the electrical master switch was on. I'd gathered by this time from the radio messages being passed from the ground that the landing strip the Daks would be using to take off from after the op had been taken with no opposition, and it was now a case of keeping it secure. Shortly before reaching the target area, we were informed that the Hunters had been in and were now on their way home.

"C-ship pulling up." This was the start of our involvement. The C-ships always pulled up a short way from the target and maintained an orbit at a pre-determined height, from where they directed the T-ships and troops and laid down covering fire to protect them. This was usually a tense moment for me, and we would be the first target that the terrs had and they would open up with everything they had. As we pulled up, I had my first sight of a terr training camp and my intense concentration and jumpiness was mingled with curiosity.

The centre of the camp was a dusty parade ground, beaten out of the red African earth. Immediately to the north were wooden buildings which might be cooking and wash-house areas, beyond which were row upon row of tents. The total area was enclosed by a high barbed wire fence with the main entrance gate on the southern perimeter. Outside the fence to the east was a collection of tents, vehicles and fuel drums: obviously the MT area.

The huts were hit

South of this were more wooden buildings, some of which had rudimentary gardens planted about them – this would be accommodation for the instructors and officers. Most importantly, scattered throughout the camp in pairs were anti-aircraft emplacements, all pointing skywards, some of them already manned.

Several of the huts had taken hits; hopefully one had been the armoury. Plenty of terrs, all of them armed, were making use of whatever cover was still available. There was a large group amongst the huts, and others were crouched in the two ditches that crossed each other along the west side of the camp. Others

Close support was provided for ground troops by Lynxes fitted with a variety of weapon loads, including 'frantans' – frangible tanks of napalm.

were manning the remainder of the anti-aircraft guns, using the emplacements as cover.

By now, a lot of small arms fire was being thrown in our direction as the all-important initial exchange of fire got under way. The chopper took one of two hits, highlighted by the sound of rounds ricocheting off metal, but all the vital bits, including ourselves, came through unscathed. I would have to have a good look round at the first available opportunity to ensure that the control rods had escaped damage.

Safety on the ground

Hitting a circling helicopter from the ground is a lot more difficult than it might at first seem. If you aim your rifle at the chopper and pull the trigger, by the time the round arrives the chopper has moved on. The trick is to aim at a position forward of the chopper; a common method was to fit a loop of wire on to the right-hand side of the weapon. If you sight the helicopter through the loop and keep your finger on the trigger long enough to empty your magazine, then at least one or two rounds will hit the chopper. A very basic form of sight, but nonetheless effective, as one round in the right place would down the chopper.

The first problem was going to be to get the T-ships safely on the ground inside the barbed wire while they were taking flak from the terrs in the ditches. C-ship 1 took up orbit slightly south of the camp, allowing C-ships 2 and 3 a clear orbit directly above the camp. The first two T-ships went inside the perimeter fence and managed to drop off their troops and get out again without taking any serious hits.

By now, the two Daks had appeared on the scene and were ready to drop the paras as directed by C-ship 1 commander. In the other two C-ships, we were busy putting down covering fire for the T-ships, taking on the anti-aircraft emplacements, avoiding the Daks and each other and generally keeping a watchful eye over the proceedings. C-ship 3 had taken some flak which had knocked out its radio junction box, cutting off their means of communication, so he was playing it by ear. One of the T-ship gunners had taken a 7.62 round in his calf and had to be casevaced out, along with several casualties from the ground forces.

The Daks had by this time dropped the paras outside the wire. These troops then broke through the wire and joined up with those already landed by the T-ships, and together they made an assault on the ditches, which they took at the first attempt.

The next objective would be the wooden huts north of the parade ground. The AA gun emplacements were by now rendered ineffective, so we could concentrate our efforts

on the larger group of terrs still resisting.

The T-ships had been busy ferrying out casevacs and parachutes and were now standing by to help ferry the troops back to the waiting Daks. After short, sharp, fierce fighting on the ground, the terrs had either all been accounted for or had taken to the bush. The decision was made to withdraw and not to engage in pursuit. With C-ships orbiting overhead, the T-ships were recalled to pick up the ground troops. Those that couldn't be picked up immediately started to make their way through the bush on foot towards the Dak landing strip.

When the Daks had their full complement of troops and wounded they took off, heading back for home. The troops who had secured the strip would be making their way back across the border on foot, unless they had bummed a lift with the Daks. One of the choppers at the strip was having problems getting its engine going; the Alouette has a complicated starting system, and it could give occasional problems that sometimes took many hours to solve.

Low on fuel

By this time, some of the terrs who had taken to the bush had regrouped and were now cautiously pursuing the withdrawing troops. C-ships 1 and 3 were dangerously low on fuel and could not remain in the vicinity any longer, so they were despatched homewards. So we now had the predicament of a chopper u/s on the ground; troops waiting to be ferried back across the border; an advancing group of terrs, who were now spread out over a long front, too widely dispersed for us in the remaining C-ship to be able to counter effectively; and ourselves getting short of fuel.

The situation was becoming slightly worrying when the T-ship radioed to say he had managed to start his engine, much to our relief. We gave him covering fire while he picked up his troops and departed, and then we too headed for home. By this time our fuel low-level warning light had been on longer than was comfortable and we decided to land as soon as we could, once back over the border, and radio for some fuel to be para-dropped to us.

This was when we found out that one of the T-ships had gone down on the way home with the loss of all six on board. Whether it had been shot down or had crashed, we never found out. Eventually our fuel arrived with enough daylight left to make it back to base, so we filled up our tank and headed for home.

Some of the Alouettes were hit by ground fire during the attack, and one went down on the way home, killing all six men on board.

Combat Skills

DECEPTION

Your drills may be correct, your weapons handling excellent but few military operations succeed without the benefit of surprise. When a Soviet officer plans an attack he includes a deception scheme as a matter of course. NATO forces must be prepared to meet this threat: remember that enemy special forces teams will infiltrate behind the lines to cause the maximum confusion.

If you can deceive your enemy over your intentions, you will dramatically increase your chances of defeating him. Battles are won by achieving surprise, and the most effective way of achieving this is by some form of deception. What exactly do we mean by 'deception in war?' The NATO definition is, "those measures designed to mislead the enemy by manipulation, distortion or falsification of evidence to induce him to react in a manner prejudicial to his interests" – in other words, pulling the wool over the enemy's eyes is likely to make him take a foolish decision. The clever use of camouflage, concealment, dummies, decoys, feints and lures, and other tricks all come under the heading of deception.

Softly, softly

The simplest form of deception is camouflage. Deception can also involve the concealment of troops in hides or on an approach march, or even on the battlefield. Many successful attacks in the past worked because the attacker had managed to move reinforcements secretly by night into the battle area without the defender's knowledge. Troops were kept under cover in towns or woods, and in the desert, where it is impossible to hide

SELLING A DUMMY

1 **When on the defensive include fake positions around your genuine trenches.**
2 **When on reconnaissance be careful not to see what the enemy wants you to see. Is that a genuine ground radar or just chicken wire and wriggly tin?**
3 **The modern battlefield is dominated by sensors – think what confuses them: use other heat sources to blur the heat signature of your own forces.**
4 **Think everything through from the enemy's point of view. Think: what would my deception plan be if I were in his position?**

troops and equipment easily, tanks were camouflaged as lorries and false concentrations of troops in dummy camps were positioned in the wrong place. You can deceive the enemy so that he does not expect an attack, or fool him that the assault will come from the wrong direction.

Dummies and decoys are other means of deception. Dummy equipment is designed to deceive enemy surveillance devices and to make him think that you are somewhere that you are not, in order to get him to attack the wrong place or to make him think you are stronger than you really are. A dummy is a simulated bit of equip-

A far-fetched example of deception perhaps, but stranger tactics have worked. Merely the planted rumours of infiltrators had Allied forces looking for German paratroops disguised as nuns in 1940. Do anything you can to waste the enemy's time and effort.

Above: An airfield is one of the hardest things to camouflage and still use, but in World War II the Germans managed to blend some of theirs into the countryside very effectively. This approach was tried on a US air base in Thailand during the Vietnam war.

Below: Experience has shown that you can get almost as good value from a dummy minefield as the real thing. To find out if it is genuine will cost the enemy valuable time and effort and the activity may well betray their presence to you.

ment, but a decoy may or may not be the real thing. Its purpose is to attract the enemy's attention and, more particularly, his fire. This could be done with a dummy tank or an abandoned real tank.

When you are in a defensive position, dummies and decoys can be useful. A complete dummy position near your real trenches can be made more realistic by positioning a mess tin to glint in the sun, by making vehicle tracks into and out of the position, and by stationing one or two men there to provide signs of movement and occupation. If at the same time you conceal your real position particularly well, the enemy will waste his fire on the wrong position and, when he attacks it, you can take him in the flank.

Smoke gets in your eyes

Smoke is a useful means of deceiving the enemy. You can use it to confuse and disorientate him, or you can advance or withdraw underneath its cover. This can be done on a grand scale – the Russians laid smoke screens hundreds of miles long during some of their major offensives in World War II – or you can produce smoke at platoon or section level with the 51-mm mortar or by using smoke grenades.

It is also possible to deceive the enemy by creating false heat sources. Modern surveillance devices, including thermal imagers and infra-red

MAKING A DUMMY DEFENSIVE POSITION

By including dummy trenches within your defensive position you can trick the enemy into attacking in the wrong direction. He then runs into your real killing zones and wastes ammo on unoccupied trenches. You can also create larger dummy defences using a handful of men to simulate a company position: giving the appearance of strength where you are weak. When creating a dummy position pay attention to the following points.

1 Siting
The dummy position must still be sited in a place that makes tactical sense. It must be far enough away from the real position so that enemy recce of the dummy does not discover it.

2 Trackplan
Enemy air recce will pick up the pattern of movement round a position very quickly. If a platoon tramps round a wood for 30 minutes on a set pattern, the disturbed ground will look like a company position from the air.

3 Routine activity
A section can easily simulate a company's worth of movement. Leave shiny objects and rubbish on the parapets of the trenches.

4 Patrol activity
Defence is always accompanied by aggressive patrolling so you must simulate a full patrol programme for the size of the dummy position with standing patrols forward to keep the enemy from actually walking on to it.

5 Fire
Ideally you should be able to cover the dummy position with direct fire weapons from your own position and the dummy should draw the enemy in to your killing areas. Register the dummy and likely enemy approach routes to it as artillery and mortar targets.

6 Thermal deception
The dummy must give the right thermal picture when scanned with a thermal imager. Small paraffin heaters can simulate human body heat and occasionally driving a vehicle around the rear of the position completes the picture.

7 Wire and mines
Marking a dummy protective minefield in front of the position and adding some obvious wiring takes little effort and can act as a very effective signpost for the enemy.

---

linescan photography, use heat to detect men, vehicles and equipment invisible to the naked eye. It is difficult to counter them by reducing the heat signature of real vehicles, but you can confuse them by putting out lots of dummy heat sources such as paraffin heaters in woods where there are no troops.

Under surveillance
You are also under surveillance from radars on the battlefield. By using anti-radar camouflage nets to hide the real vehicles and creating false echoes elsewhere, you can confuse the enemy very easily. Radio traffic can be used to simulate non-existent formations of troops; radio operators located in a particular area talking to each other about fictitious plans for a counter-attack can successfully simulate the real thing. Even if the ruse only lasts for a few days or even hours before being uncovered as a hoax, it may provide the vital extra time that you need to mount a successful attack elsewhere.

Another variation is for false information to be provided over real radio nets in the hope that the enemy will be listening in. In fast-moving modern warfare this sort of ruse is less likely to happen, but even at platoon level you could be part of some larger deception plan of this sort.

Combat engineers may be involved in some larger deception measures.

Above: *To conceal the evacuation from Gallipoli, British and ANZAC forces used a version of the water clock to fire rifles at intervals throughout the night. They were still firing when all the troops were safely embarked and the Turks did not know what was happening.*

Below: *A US Army HAWK surface-to-air missile launcher deployed during exercises in Egypt. In very open terrain total concealment is difficult, so fake positions and dummy kit play a vital role. The RAF uses purpose built dummy Rapier launchers.*

Combat Skills

Dummy trenches

Include these dummy trenches when preparing a defensive position:

1 Four-man main battle trenches

Any suitable hillock or mound can be converted by cutting firing ports and chopping the grass covering the mound into segments to simulate split-locking. Dig out the entry point to a depth of 30 cm to give the correct amount of shadow. Clear obvious fields of fire to the front and rear of the trench and don't forget to include the dummy in the trackplan.

2 Open slit trenches

A slit trench with shelter bay can be simulated by digging a shallow trench 15 cm deep and placing black hessian in the bottom. Fill several sandbags to form the parapet and then spend a few minutes flattening the surrounding vegetation with muddy boots. Hasty positions in woods can be put together using logs and brushwood and sloppy use of surplus camnets.

Radio deception

Enemy forces will monitor your radio net. Intercepted messages invite shelling, jamming or even the transmission of fake orders. Avoid these problems by the following:

1 Use woods, hills and buildings to screen your transmissions from the enemy.

2 Transmit your message on the lowest power possible that allows efficient communication.

3 Do not use unofficial codes or nicknames or illicit chat nets! Stick rigidly to the rules of Battle Code.

4 Keep your messages as short as possible.

5 Make full use of alternative means of communication, such as line, civilian telephone or runners.

6 Enforce radio silence wherever possible on operations.

7 Move the radio as often as possible.

8 Avoid using radio check messages and do not get into the habit of squelching – pressing the 'pressel' switch on the radio to check it works before you go on the air before an operation. This warns the enemy that something major is about to happen.

Jamming and deception

Jamming

Learn to recognise the different forms of jamming so you can distinguish jamming from defective equipment or failing batteries. If you suspect jamming check all the radio equipment to make sure it is not an internal fault, or there is another radio set transmitting close enough to cause interference. If you are being jammed:

1 Check the tuning of the radio and then try to work through the jamming signal.

2 If communication is impossible turn up the power and fit a larger antenna.

3 Send a jamming report by alternative means and carry out any anti-jamming plans you have been given.

Radio deception

Slick radio procedure and good net discipline is the best defence against deception. If the enemy interceptor listening in hears that all stations on the net are answering promptly in the correct order and are using the correct procedures and codes he is unlikely to attempt to break into the net.

If you suspect that a message is bogus do not be afraid to use the authentication table on your battlecode sheet to check out the station sending the message. Any instruction over the radio that does not seem to fit in to the overall plan of action should also be checked. When you are sure a station is bogus send a deception report by secure alternative means in the same way as the jamming report.

For instance, during an advance or withdrawal an army depends to a very large extent on the bridges it has erected over rivers for its logistic support. A large number of dummy bridges may well divert and waste enemy bombing effort. Dummy missile positions on airfields can make it more difficult for enemy pilots to locate and eliminate the real ones: the RAF Regiment is actually equipped with Dummy Rapier missile launchers.

Behind the front

Behind the front line there are a larger number of sizeable and static installations on which you may depend for support: airfields, missile sites or logistic depots. Although the enemy knows exactly where they are they can still be concealed to some extent. Parallel runways and dummy aircraft can be generated on airfields to mislead the pilots of attacking aircraft.

Other methods such as coloured foam (which lasts for several days) can

The Germans are past masters at deception. Unfortunately this includes the East Germans, who maintain a unit equipped with US tanks and APCs supplied by North Vietnam. They wear West German uniforms and look indistinguishable from our NATO allies.

DECEPTION ON D-DAY

A comprehensive deception plan played a key role in the success of the Allied invasion of France in June 1944. Hitler expected the attack to be made in the Pas de Calais, not Normandy. To encourage him in this belief the Allies deceived German intelligence that a vast US Army Group was deployed in Kent ready to pounce on Calais. Radio-equipped vans drove around the country generating a heavy volume of signal traffic while the real invasion force assembled to the west in strict silence.

Dummy camps and depots were built around Dover and the famous US general Patton was announced as the commander of '1st US Army Group' and (much to his irritation) had to keep touring his mythical command. The deception succeeded so well that the Germans held back large reserves to cover Calais even after the Normandy landings, which the High Command suspected were a feint designed to trick them!

The increase in intelligence gathering equipment since World War II theoretically makes this sort of scheme harder to pull off. However, although modern intelligence systems are capable of gathering a more accurate picture of enemy activities, all data is ultimately checked by a human brain. Show someone what they want to see or expect to see and the deception is under way.

be used to remove such key indicators as road junctions, perimeter tracks, runways and the like, confusing pilots for a few vital seconds during their run-in for an attack. It is necessary for the pilot of a modern jet attacking this sort of target to achieve visual detection at four kilometres if he is going to make an effective attack. At four kilometres' range, flying at 100 ft above the ground and closing at 500 knots, what catches the pilot's eye? Perhaps the perimeter fence and track, roads and other paved surfaces including the access road, the pattern of buildings, equipment in the open and prominent landmarks near the base. Much can be done to tone down all these telltale signs. The perimeter can be made less obvious by having the same type of ground on each side of it – for instance, if there is a ploughed field outside the perimeter then the ground inside should also be ploughed. Trees can be planted to break up the outline of buildings and to hide access roads. If roads cannot be hidden, they should be made to appear part of the civil system, and false roofs can be put on a large flat-roofed building to make it look like a row of houses. None of this is guaranteed to provide total anonymity, but it may help a great deal.

Whether you are an infantryman in

a front-line trench or a storeman in a base depot, deception affects you. Give it some thought. Deceiving and surprising the enemy may be the crucial factor that gives you the advantage and makes the difference between winning and losing.

This is an M551 Sheridan tank converted to look like a BMP as part of the US army's 'Soviet' training forces. This sort of conversion is too time-consuming for field use, so some companies now make blow-up rubber tanks which look like the real thing from a distance.

Battle Fitness Programme No. 7

THE IMPORTANCE OF WARMING UP

It is very important to warm up before taking vigorous exercise. By spending between five and ten minutes warming up you prepare your body for exercise, which helps to prevent muscle tears and strains occurring during the work-out. Warming up performs three main functions:

1 Gently stretches of your muscles
2 Puts your joints through a full range of movement
3 Increases heart rate and circulation

A slow start

By doing 6-8 gentle warm-up exercises all your major muscle groups will be stretched, ready for action, but don't get carried away and do exercises like push-ups or pull-ups which will build up lactic acid in your muscles and create an 'oxygen debt' – not a good start to your work-out. You must stick to low-intensity exercises that will not tire your muscles.

Your warm-up exercises should involve the joints in a full range of movement: particularly important since tight joints are very susceptible to injury during physical activity owing to their limited range of movement. By feeling looser you will enjoy

1 Arm circling
Stand with your feet apart, trunk upright, and circle your arms so that they almost touch your ears. Repeat 10-15 times.

2 Trunk turning and arm flinging
Stand with your feet wide apart and gently turn your trunk to alternate sides with your arms outstretched. Repeat 10 times each side.

3 Side bends
With your feet apart and your hands on your hips, bend your trunk sideways while keeping your shoulders square to the front and your head up. Repeat 10 times each side.

4 Quadriceps stretch
Stand on one leg and bend your other knee up while holding your ankle. Pull gently towards your buttock for a gentle stretch and repeat three times for each leg.

5 Knee to chest
Standing on one leg, pull alternate knees into your chest with your arms. Keep your trunk upright and pull in for 8-10 seconds. Repeat six times on each leg.

bend trunk right
bend trunk left
right leg
left leg

right knee into chest
left knee into chest

622

your work-out much more and your body will move more economically.

Just as you would not dream of driving a car at 70 mph in the first few seconds, neither should you push your body into 'overdrive' before it is fully prepared. Your heart rate should be gently increased from its normal resting rate (about 72 beats per minute) up to an exercise starting rate of 90 to 100 beats a minute. This will allow more blood to be pumped to the working muscles in a progressive manner as well as providing them with the necessary fuel and oxygen. The blood vessels will also open up to allow increased blood-flow to all working muscles. Your body temperature will increase one or two degrees but not enough to cause a state of fatigue.

Another important aspect of the warm-up is getting a good 'mind-set' for your work-out. Your warm-up clears the mind, allowing you to forget the strains and stresses of the past day or two. Concentrate only on what you are going to do in your work-out: the planned exercises, heart rate levels, jogging route etc. It is also useful to remind yourself of all the benefits that the work-out will bring and then there is only one thing left – do it!

6 Calf stretch

Place one foot behind the other with your feet parallel and the heel of your back foot flat on the ground. Bend the forward knee gently until you feel it lightly stretched. Hold for a count of 10 and repeat three times on each leg.

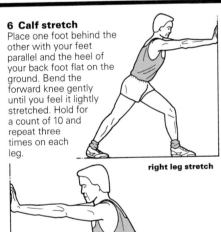

right leg stretch

left leg stretch

7 Hamstring stretch

Stand on one leg and place the other in front on a support. Bend forward from the waist and reach forward towards the raised foot until you feel a gentle stretch. Hold for a count of 10 and repeat three times on each leg.

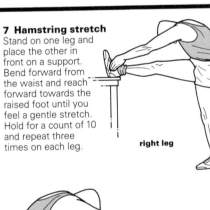

right leg

left leg

8 Warm-up jog

Take an easy jog for 2-3 minutes with one or two short sprints. This completes the warm-up, easing your body into physical activity in a safe and enjoyable manner.

short sprint

2-3 minutes jogging

AEROBIC EXERCISE – THE KEY TO PEAK FITNESS

There are many methods of keeping fit, but none are as important as aerobic fitness. Aerobic means 'with oxygen', and it is the key to surviving modern sedentary living and enjoying a healthily energetic life. The aim of aerobic exercise is to improve those organs and systems involved in your body's processing of oxygen: the heart, lungs and blood vessels.

Use of oxygen

An improvement in the functioning of these areas leads to better utilization of oxygen and a much fitter individual.

The principal aerobic activity is jogging. Millions of people all over the world go for a daily jog: why do they do this, and what are the benefits?

Benefits of aerobic exercise

Your aerobic fitness is the ability of your respiratory and circulatory systems to supply oxygen during sustained physical activity. A good level of aerobic fitness provides many benefits, including:
1 Increased heart efficiency
2 Increased lung efficiency
3 Reduction in body fat
4 Reduction in cholesterol
5 Release of stress and tension

Aerobic exercise increases the ability of your heart and lungs to supply oxygen to the blood. Running is one of the most effective of this type of exercise.

1 Heart efficiency

The heart is a muscle which, like all other muscles, thrives on physical activity. It grows stronger with the right kind of exercise and weaker without it. A strong, trained heart can get more oxygen-carrying blood to your other muscles by beating faster and more powerfully. Muscles require oxygen to work and if they do not receive enough they quickly become tired. The ability of your heart to pump blood is critically important during exercise especially, if the activity is sustained.

2 Lung efficiency

Aerobic exercise increases the efficiency of your lungs and also strengthens the muscles that make the lungs expand and contract. Oxygen is collected by the blood as it passes through the lungs, and then carried to the working muscles. If your lungs are not healthy (for example, due to smoking) oxygen cannot be collected efficiently, reducing your ability to exercise for long periods.

3 Reduction in body fat

Many people are overweight through a lack of physical activity, and obesity is a major coronary risk factor because it imposes extra work on your heart. Regular aerobic exercise at a moderate intensity increases the rate at which you burn up calories, which results in a lower percentage of body fat. This can be achieved through a regular programme of aerobic activity lasting 20 to 30 minutes, three to five times a week.

4 Reduction in cholesterol

If you do not take regular exercise your body is likely to produce more low density lipoprotein (LDL) cholesterol, which leads eventually to heart disease. Physically active people appear to produce more of the higher-density lipoprotein (HDL) cholesterol, which scavenges the LDL 'bad' cholesterol and transports it to your liver for disposal. Studies show that to produce a high level of HDL you need to jog at least 15 miles a week.

5 Release of stress and tension

High levels of stress are strongly linked with unnecessary tiredness, illness and premature heart disease. If you are highly tensed your body becomes chemically out of balance through the increase in stress hormones such as adrenalin. Aerobic exercise is nature's tranquillizer, and by re-distributing the stress hormones it brings the mind and body closer together for a natural feeling of well-being.

Aerobic fitness builds up stamina and endurance, vital for soldiers such as Royal Marines who have to be able to carry heavy loads over great distances. By training your heart and lungs to work more effectively you won't tire so quickly during strenuous exercise.

The principles of aerobic exercise

1 Frequency

Beginners should work out aerobically 2-3 times a week, building up to 4-5 times a week for peak fitness.

2 Intensity

You should exercise hard enough to increase heart and breathing activity to between 60 and 80 per cent of maximum capacity. Lower than 60 per cent does not provide good training effect unless you are monstrously unfit. Higher than 80 per cent takes you into anaerobic ('without oxygen') exercise, which you will not be able to maintain for long periods. In Part 9 of the Battle Fitness Programme we will show you how to check your pulse rate.

Swimming is another good aerobic exercise although, unlike this Royal Marine, you do not have to do it with a rifle!

3 Duration

To get the full benefits of aerobic exercise you will need at least 20 minutes of moderate/high intensity activity. This should increase to 30-45 minutes if you are very fit and 45-60 when you are at peak fitness.

4 Type of activity

The most effective activities are high-energy exercises including running, jogging, swimming, cycling and cross-country ski-ing. These activities place the necessary demands on your body and train your vital aerobic systems.

Peak fitness
Aerobic exercise is of enormous benefit, physically and mentally. Whatever your starting level, regular aerobic training can lead you to peak fitness in the shortest possible time.

Battle Fitness Programme No. 9

TRAINING YOUR HEART

Your heart is the most important trainable muscle in your body. It is easily taken for granted and neglected, which leads to disease and premature ageing. A weak heart can have difficulty supplying sufficient oxygen to your muscles, which means you become tired quickly.

By exercising regularly you can train your heart to become strong and efficient, and it does not take very much time and effort to keep it at peak fitness. In order to get the best results from your training you need to check that your heart is working at the most effective rate. You should monitor your pulse rate at regular intervals, which will also ensure that you are exercising at a safe level.

Depending on your age, you have a personal 'training zone', often referred to as your 'target heart rate'. it is a level of activity high enough to provide sufficient exercise to strengthen the heart, but not uncomfortably high (and possibly dangerous for someone who is unfit). In most cases, the ideal level is between 70 and 85 per cent of your maximum heart rate.

Running can place a great strain on your heart and lungs. If you force your heart to work near its maximum rate you will simply exhaust yourself and not achieve much benefit from the exercise. At the other extreme, a very gentle jog is unlikely to increase your fitness. You must aim to get your heart working at about three-quarters of its maximum rate, monitoring your pulse while you exercise. By paying attention to your heart rate you will get the best results from your training.

How to calculate your target heart rate

You can calculate and monitor your target heart-rate by using the following formula. This is very simple to do and will provide you with a personal target for your training, which should help your motivation.

The formula

1 For the beginner exerciser:
220 minus **your age** multiplied by **60 per cent**

2 For the regular exerciser:
220 minus **your age** multiplied by **70 per cent**

3 For the advanced exerciser:
220 minus **your age** multiplied by **85 per cent**

You can also refer to the chart provided.

Use this formula and chart to find out what your heart rate should be while you are exercising. As you become fitter your target heart rate will increase.

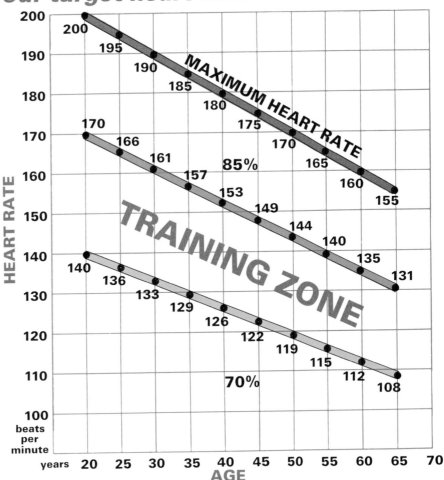

Taking your pulse

To keep your heart within your target heart-rate zone you need to know how to take your own pulse. This can be done by touching either your wrist or the carotid artery on the side of your neck; the latter is generally easier during training. Place your first two fingers on the artery while you exercise and count the number of beats over a 15-second period. Multiply by four to give the number of beats per minute: i.e. 30 beats per 15 seconds means you have a heart rate of 120 BPM.

As explained in Part 8 of the Battle Fitness Programme, the key to improving your heart's performance is aerobic exercise such as jogging or swimming. Remember to spend 5-10 minutes warming up first. About half an hour's aerobic exercise taken three to five times a week will make all the difference. You may find it difficult at first but you will improve if you keep at it, and by monitoring your heart rate you will ensure that you are getting the maximum benefit from your exercise sessions.

Take your pulse by pressing your fingers on the inside of your wrist to the left, just behind your thumb.

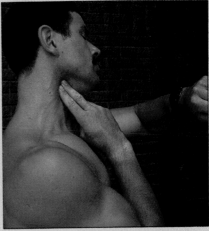

When taking your pulse during exercise it is often easier to press the carotid artery in your neck.

RPG-7: Rocket from Russia

An Egyptian soldier peers through the optical sights of an RPG-7 with no missile fitted to the launcher. The Egyptian and Syrian armies demonstrated the effectiveness of massed RPGs against Israeli armour in 1973, using them for close-range protection of their anti-tank missile groups and in specialist tank-hunting groups.

The RPG-7 is, along with its successor, the RPG-16, the main weapon of the Soviet soldier against enemy tanks. They are supplemented by the RPG-18, a copy of the M72 66-mm light anti-tank weapon used by US, British and many other forces. The earlier RPG-2, while still in widespread use in China and Vietnam, is no longer a front-line Soviet weapon.

But it is not just the Soviet army that uses RPG-7s, which is why familiarity with the RPG-7 and its operation is a good idea. As your enemies (or allies) may be equipped with them, captured or borrowed RPG-7s can be a worthwhile addition to your firepower, not just in the anti-tank role but against a wide range of targets. An RPG-7 is a useful thing to have in an infantry firefight.

RPG-7s have a long combat record. In the 1973 Middle East War, they destroyed more Israeli tanks on the northern front than any other weapon. The

Israelis themselves have adopted large numbers of captured RPG-7s, and have designed and produced a similar weapon.

In Vietnam, RPGs were the second-biggest killer of Allied armour, after mines. In Afghanistan the Soviets have lost many tanks to RPG-7s, especially in the first year of the war. Meanwhile, the Soviets themselves use RPG-7s in Afghanistan against the drystone sangars (breastworks) used by the Resistance instead of foxholes.

Arming and aiming the RPG-7

To use an RPG-7, you first start by assembling the grenade: either the PG-7 HEAT (High-Explosive Anti-Tank, the standard round), the improved long-nose PG-7M, or the OG-7 High Explosive rounds, screwing the warhead and sustainer motor with the booster charge. These are normally carried, four to a haversack, by the gunner and assistant gunner.

The assembled round loads into the muzzle of the RPG launcher. This whole procedure takes about 14 seconds.

The gunner sights in on his target. The optical sight on the RPG-7 is a relatively complex piece of equipment and does not have the usual Soviet degree of soldier-proofing. It should not be carried on the weapon while on the move, but in its carrying case or in some other secure container.

A rangefinding stadia is marked on the RPG-7's optical sights. The gunner places the stadia's baseline on the tank's treads. The mark reached by the turret top shows the range in hundreds of metres. The big drawback is that the system only works properly if the target tank is 2.7 metres high: if it is not, or is occupying a hull-down position with only the turret exposed you are in trouble, and must use a memorized formula or, more likely, a good guess.

How to fire an RPG-7

1 Screw the warhead and sustainer motor together with the booster charge.

2 Estimate the range of the target using the stadia sights.

3 Aim the rocket using the grid below the boresight mark, adjusting your aim according to the target's speed and the wind velocity.

4 If possible, fire as soon as the target comes within 300 metres. This gives you a fair chance of a hit and allows time for a second shot.

5 Observe where the rocket went, reload and fire again. With practice you can get another round off within 15 seconds.

6 Unless there is a pressing reason to stay where you are, move to another firing position since the RPG's backblast will betray your position to the enemy.

metres, at which range the round has a relatively flat trajectory and, in case of a miss, you might have time for another round before the tank grinds you into the mud.

Against non-moving tanks or in a situation where you have to get a round off fast, use the 'iron' tangent sights on the front of the weapon. Similar to these on the 66-mm M72 LAW, these sights have elevation lines but lack the elaborate rangefinding and deflection lines. If you know

Right: An Iranian soldier fires an RPG-7 at an Iraqi position in Khorramshar, the backblast of the rocket kicking up a huge cloud of dust.

Below: A Soviet soldier takes aim with his RPG-7, covered by a comrade armed with an AKM assault rifle. When a Soviet Motor Rifle infantry section dismounts from its BMP the RPG-7 gunner is stationed in the middle, next to the section commander.

The Chinese have provided two range-finding reticles on their home-made version of the RPG-7, one for Soviet-size tanks and one for larger Western-built tanks, making the gunner's task easier. The Afghan Resistance, who use both Soviet- and Chinese-built versions of the RPG-7, think the Chinese ammunition is better and has fewer mis-fires.

Once he has found the range, an RPG gunner elevates his weapon to get the proper trajectory, determining this by the range lines marked on his sight at 100-metre intervals from 200 to 500 (the maximum) metres.

The most difficult part about aiming an RPG-7 is leading a moving target, especially in a crosswind. The fin-stabilized, rocket-propelled RPG-7 round has a tendency to turn into the wind, and the gunner must calculate that as well, which is difficult if the tank is moving at right angles to the gunner.

Optimum range for RPG is 300

A veteran member of the Afghan resistance movement demonstrates the correct prone firing position with the RPG-16 to fellow Mujahideen. This is an improved model of the basic RPG-7, with a bipod for steadier shooting and a warhead with better armour penetration.

Inside the RPG-7

The RPG-7 is one of the most common anti-tank weapons in the world, carried by every Soviet infantry section and widely used by guerrilla and terrorist forces from Kabul to Crossmaglen. Its accuracy is very dependent on the ability of the gunner, and it is unable to penetrate the Chobham armour fitted to the British Challenger and US M1 Abrams. However, it is effective against conventionally-armoured vehicles and has proved a valuable weapon in urban combat.

Stabilizing fins
These snap open after the missile is launched and, together with the small fins at the very end of the missile, impart a slow roll to the round on its way to the target.

'Iron' sights
These tangent sights no wind or deflection adjustment, and are supposed to be used when you have to fire hurry and there isn't enough time to use the optical sights. However, for the average man clearing the optical equipment is far too complex and most guerrillas rely exclusively on the iron sights.

Piezo-electric fuse
This produces a voltage when the nose is crushed against an inner skin by the rocket impacting against a tank's armour.

Warhead
The shaped charge anti-tank warhead is very fast acting, a mixture of 94 per cent RDX and 6 per cent wax. It arms itself after the missile has travelled five metres.

Copper liner
This is moulded by the explosion and helps form the warhead's explosive jet which burns through 330mm of conventional armour plate.

Motor
This fires after the missile has travelled 10 metres from the firer and it burns until the rocket has travelled 500 metres.

Tail of the PG-7 round
This must be screwed on to the body before firing.

Tri

or can estimate the range to the target, flip these sights up, and elevate the RPG as required.

Firing the RPG

Before firing, the gunner or his assistant must make sure the 30-metre backblast area is clear. The RPG-7 has a particularly nasty backblast, and the hospitals around Peshawar all have Afghan guerrillas who have mishandled RPGs.

Look out for rocks that will be blown by the blast, or walls that will bounce the blast back to you: at least two metres clearance is required for walls. If you are looking to scare away a helicopter or otherwise pointing the RPG skywards, be especially careful, as the blast may hit the ground by your feet. The RPG-7 may be fired prone (feet must be kept out of the backblast), kneeling or standing, and it must be fired from the right shoulder. The backblast from launching the round from the tube is a one-metre ball of smoke which remains for up to eight seconds, so it may also have the effect of drawing enemy fire.

Safety precautions

Before firing, make sure the breech cover has been removed and that the breech is not resting against the ground or any other object, and that nothing is clogging it.

Once the gunner squeezes the trigger, it ignites a powder charge, ejecting the grenade from the tube at a speed of 84 metres per second. The four stabilizing fins pop open as the round is ejected. Soviet ammunition leaves a great deal to be desired.

If one of the grenade's fins fails to deploy, dive for cover. If you have a mis-fire or a hangfire, keep the thing pointed down-range. Do not use rounds that look to be mis-handled or have been dropped on their nose.

The warhead arms after the grenade has travelled five metres and, after 11 metres, the sustainer rocket ignites, producing a bright flash and puff of smoke and boosting the grenade to a maximum velocity of 294 metres per second. If it does not hit anything in five seconds, the round self-destructs.

If it does hit something, the piezo-electric fuse in the nose will detonate

Using the optical sight

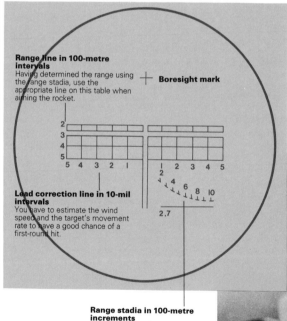

Range line in 100-metre intervals
Having determined the range using the range stadia, use the appropriate line on this table when aiming the rocket.

Boresight mark

Lead correction line in 10-mil intervals
You have to estimate the wind speed and the target's movement rate to have a good chance of a first-round hit.

Range stadia in 100-metre increments
This is based on the assumption that the target is a high NATO tank, 2.7 metres tall. Use the stadia markings to bracket the tank and work out the range; obviously, the closer the enemy the higher it will appear in the sight picture. It is only worth a shot once within 300 metres (the second mark from the left).

The optical sight fitted to Soviet RPG-7s is specifically designed used against Western tanks, which higher than Soviet ones. The sight a simple scale to help you judge range and a grid to help you aim according to target speed and d

This Soviet soldier is using the optical sight as described here. Because it is hard to allow for wind speed and target movement, many soldiers give up and rely on the simpler iron sights provided.

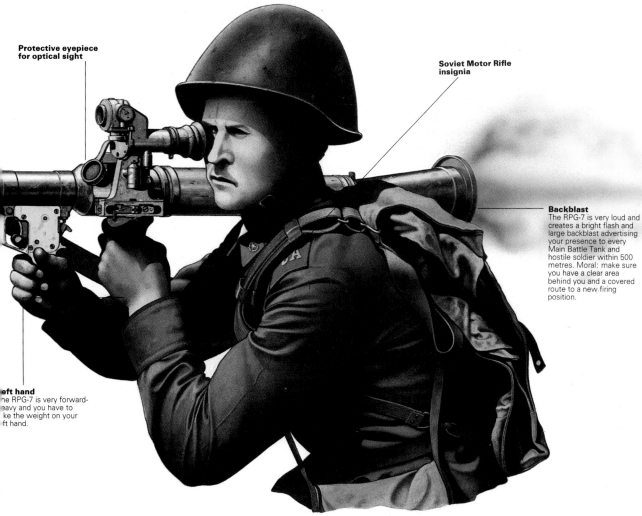

Protective eyepiece for optical sight

Soviet Motor Rifle insignia

Backblast
The RPG-7 is very loud and creates a bright flash and large backblast advertising your presence to every Main Battle Tank and hostile soldier within 500 metres. Moral: make sure you have a clear area behind you and a covered route to a new firing position.

eft hand
he RPG-7 is very forward-eavy and you have to ke the weight on your ft hand.

the shaped charge warhead. The PG-7 can punch a five-centimetre hole through 280 mm of armour plate, shooting hot explosive gases and equally hot metal fragments into the target, to be followed, milliseconds later, by the copper charge liner.

A PG-7 round will go through any armour on a US Army M60 main battle tank, but not an M1 Abrams or a Challenger. It will also penetrate 23 cm of sandbags, 45.7 cm of reinforced concrete, and 150.4 cm of earth and log bunker. What will reduce its effectiveness greatly is improved armour, such as the Chobham-type compound armour used on the latest NATO main battle tanks or Israeli Blazer reactive armour.

Anti-personnel use

The RPG-7 is effective against infantry too, and makes a useful anti-sniper weapon. It can provide supporting firepower within its 300 m flat-trajectory range – certainly within the range of most firefights.

The OG-7 HE-Frag round, which uses the same fuse as a Soviet 82-mm mortar round, would be particularly effective. Each RPG user can put

down fire with the punch of a medium mortar and the accuracy of a direct-fire weapon.

In urban combat, RPGs can be extremely effective – in Hue, 1968, two US Marine battalion commanders stated that RPGs were the most dangerous weapon their troops faced.

Tactics

In the Soviet army, the RPG-7 gunner is normally positioned, in the attack or defence, next to the squad leader, so that he can direct the gunner's fire. Because of the limited effec-

tive range of the RPG – especially when compared to a tank's main gun or machine-gun – camouflage, concealment and surprise are needed to get close to a tank.

The Soviets stress the use of 'fire pockets' and anti-tank ambushes to make the RPG an effective anti-tank weapon despite its limited range. Thus, whenever possible, RPGs will

The RPG-7 has been used in almost every armed conflict in the last 20 years. This African guerrilla is using his RPG-7 without the complex optical sight, a common practice in irregular forces.

be positioned to take advantage of other weapons. For example, a tank turning to avoid a minefield would turn its flanks to concealed RPGs, or RPGs may be positioned to hit tanks going through a gap in a minefield while in column formation.

Protecting dead space

RPGs can also be used to protect the 'dead space' close to ATGMs. When thinking how to deploy your RPG-7s, think how it will work together with all your other tank-killing weapons.

RPG-7 gunners in marching order with their rounds, which need their tails screwing on, in their right hands. Later models of the launcher can be folded.

Anti-tank ambushes can also be used as an offensive tactic. Creeping up on armoured units in night positions and using RPG-7s with the NSP-2 night sight has been one way to kill enemy tanks. The North Vietnamese during Operation 'Junction City' in 1967 and the Afghan guerrillas in the Panjsher V offensive in 1982 both used RPG-7s effectively in this way. In the Panjsher, the Afghans used the RPGs together with light machine-guns, allowing each team that infiltrated close to the Soviet night positions to deal with either an armoured or unarmoured threat.

RPGs have frequently been used against helicopters in Rhodesia, Viet-

Battlefield Evaluation: comparing

40-mm RPG-7

Firing a muzzle-loaded 85-mm (in the standard PG-7 version) grenade, the RPG-7 will be seen in trouble spots around the world for many years to come. It is produced in the Soviet Union, China, and a number of licensed and unlicensed Third World nations. Both sides in the Iran-Iraq war have made extensive use of RPG-7s. Ironically, today RPG-7s are used more often against Communist forces – in Afghanistan, Nicaragua, and Angola – than by them.

Specification:
Launcher weight: 7.9 kg
Round weight: 2.25 kg
Muzzle velocity: 120 m per second
Maximum velocity: 300 m per second
Effective range: 300 m
Armour penetration: 330 mm

Assessment
Reliability ★★★
Accuracy ★★
Age ★★★★★
Worldwide users ★★★★★

A Soviet section ready for action, with AKM rifles set for single-shot and a PK machine gun.

84-mm M2 Carl Gustav

This Swedish-designed recoilless rifle remains in service worldwide, including the British and Canadian armies as the standard section medium anti-tank weapon. Unlike the US Army, which uses the M47 Dragon ATGM as its medium anti-tank weapon, these armies, like the Soviets, have continued to keep an unguided anti-tank weapon with the fighting troops. It has a higher potential rate of fire than the RPG-7.

Specification:
Launcher weight: 14.2 kg
Round weight: 1.7 kg
Muzzle velocity: 310 m per second
Maximum velocity: 310 m per second
Effective range: 450 m
Armour penetration: 450 mm

Assessment
Reliability ★★★★
Accuracy ★★★
Age ★★★★★
Worldwide users ★★★★

The 84 'Charlie 6' is usually used one per section in the British Army, and is more cumbersome than the RPG-7.

82-mm B-300

Developed from the RPG-7 and the French LRAC 89, this Israeli system's innovation is that it consists of two parts: a re-usable sight and gripstock, connected to the muzzle, to which the rounds, packed in the disposable tubes that include the breech, are inserted before firing. It fires rocket-powered fin-stabilized rounds. The B-300 has been ordered by the US Marine Corps as an anti-bunker and anti-tank weapon.

Specification:
Launcher weight: 3.5 kg
Round weight: 4.5 kg
Muzzle velocity: 280 m per second
Maximum velocity: over 280 m per second
Effective range: 400 m
Armour penetration: 400+ mm

Assessment
Reliability ★★★★
Accuracy ★★★
Age ★★
Worldwide users ★★

The B-300 is an excellent weapon, useful for bunker busting as well as destroying enemy armour.

nam and, now, in Afghanistan. While aiming is difficult against a moving helicopter, hovering helicopters are vulnerable. Although firing RPG-7s against armed enemy helicopters may expose your position and leave you vulnerable to a devastating counter-strike without having much chance of killing it first, it is likely to make a heli-copter pilot think he is being shot at with man-portable surface-to-air mis-siles, and so the RPG-7 can have a deterrent effect in the anti-helicopter role.

***US** soldiers training on the **RPG-7** are using the new **PG-7M** warhead, which entered service in about 1980 and is longer and thinner than the original.*

the RPG-7 with its rivals

80-mm Folgore

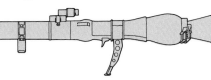

The standard MAW of the Italian army, the Folgore fires a rocket-propelled, fin-stabilized round. Heavier than the RPG-7, making it primarily a two-man weapon, it is also capable of longer range anti-tank fire. While this is a good idea for the Italian army (whose operational role is primarily defensive against an armoured threat), it is less useful for those looking for a weapon that can be carried through the area of operations to provide supporting firepower in case of a firefight.

Specification:
Launcher weight: 18.9 kg
Round weight: 3 kg
Muzzle velocity: 380 m per second
Maximum velocity: 500 m per second
Effective range: 1000 m
Armour penetration: unknown

Assessment
Reliability	★★★★
Accuracy	★★★
Age	★★★
Worldwide users	★

A much heavier weapon than the RPG-7, Folgore is primarily a defensive weapon.

60-mm Panzerfaust 3

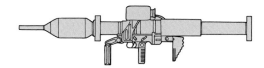

The state-of-the-art in light anti-tank weapons, along with the British 80-mm LAW, this will take over many of the roles associated with medium anti-tank weapons in the past. Muzzle-loaded and firing an oversize 110-mm round, the Panzerfaust 3 will become the standard LAW of the West German army. Unlike the RPG-7 or RPG-16, it has an ogive head on its HEAT warhead, allowing for better stand-off when detonating.

Specification:
Launcher weight: 12 kg
Round weight: 3.8 kg
Muzzle velocity: 170 m per second
Maximum velocity: 250 m per second
Effective range: 500 m
Armour penetration: (estimated) 700 mm

Assessment
Reliability	★★★★
Accuracy	★★★★
Age	★
Worldwide users	★★

Panzerfaust 3 is the new West German anti-tank weapon, relatively light but very powerful.

120-mm SEP DARD 120

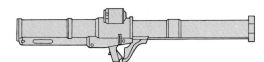

Developed by the French, the DARD 120 is the 'big game hunter's' choice among modern man-portable unguided anti-armour systems. Its calibre – larger than that of any other of these weapons – is intended to give it a better chance of killing a modern main battle tank from the front. Probably neither a Carl Gustav, nor an RPG-7, nor an RPG-16, can knock out a modern tank from the front, but the DARD can penetrate the NATO Heavy Triple Target. Like the B-300 and the Panzerfaust 3, it consists of a re-usable sight and gripstock.

Specification:
Launcher weight: 4.5 kg
Round weight: 8.9 kg
Muzzle velocity: 280 m per second
Maximum velocity: 280 m per second
Effective range: 600 m
Armour penetration: 500+ mm

Assessment
Reliability	★★★★
Accuracy	★★★★
Age	★
Worldwide users	★

SEP DARD is the most powerful shoulder-fired unguided anti-tank weapon available today.

Crashing into Action with
M113

In the summer of 1961 Viet Cong units fighting in the Mekong Delta suffered a series of surprise defeats at the hands of government troops equipped with new armoured vehicles. These large olive-drab machines roared across the paddy fields emitting clouds of fumes and smoke and spraying the guerrillas with heavy machine-gun fire. To the US Army who had supplied them they were M113 Armoured Personnel Carriers, but to the panic-stricken VC they were 'Green Dragons', sinister machines to be treated with respect.

The M113 was first used in action by South Vietnamese troops and American advisers. Here an early model M113 crosses a bridge in the Mekong Delta during November 1962.

While it did not take long for the Viet Cong to develop tactics to use against the M113, their shortage of anti-tank weapons made this simple APC a very effective weapon in the early years of the US involvement in South East Asia.

From its inception the M113 was designed to be a jack-of-all-trades. The original US Army specification called for a lightweight, amphibious and air-droppable APC with good cross-country performance. By application

of kits and modifications of the basic chassis a generation of support vehicles could be created, all sharing the same automotive parts. By 1987 the M113 had become the most widely used armoured fighting vehicle in the world. Over 50 armies are equipped with it, and most have converted it to suit their own special requirements.

The M113 followed a number of US Army APCs, all of simple box-like design, for transporting the infantry to battle. The armour protection was designed to defeat small arms and shell splinters but nothing more; the infantry squad riding in the vehicle was supposed to dismount to assault an enemy position while the APC provided supporting fire with its .50-cal machine-gun. However, as it received its combat debut in Vietnam, mounted action seemed to offer exciting possibilities.

Combat experience soon led to a number of alterations in the M113's design. Most significantly, the petrol engine, which was a serious fire

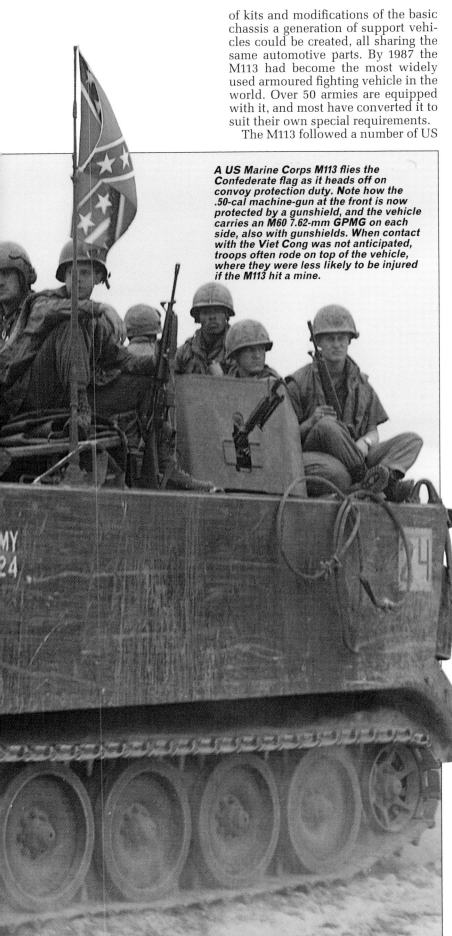

A US Marine Corps M113 flies the Confederate flag as it heads off on convoy protection duty. Note how the .50-cal machine-gun at the front is now protected by a gunshield, and the vehicle carries an M60 7.62-mm GPMG on each side, also with gunshields. When contact with the Viet Cong was not anticipated, troops often rode on top of the vehicle, where they were less likely to be injured if the M113 hit a mine.

M-125 self-propelled 81-mm mortars of the 11th Armored Cavalry Regiment prepare to bombard Hill 95 near Quan Loi, III Corps Military Zone, in June 1970.

hazard in a damaged vehicle, was replaced by a diesel. Unlike petrol, diesel fuel will not be ignited by a penetrating anti-tank round.

M113s in Vietnam soon began to appear very different from the gleaming vehicles equipping US units in Europe; the APC's uncluttered box shape vanished beneath a pile of sandbags, ammunition boxes and spare track blocks all placed to detonate a shaped charge anti-tank round before it struck the armour and thus reduce its ability to penetrate.

The M113's armament of one .50-cal machine-gun was soon supplemented in Vietnam. Christened the Armoured Cavalry Assault Vehicle, its machine-gun protected by a gunshield and back plate and with a pair of 7.62-mm M60s or Browning .30 cals fitted to the sides firing from the crew compartment, the M113 went to war. Subsequently the vehicle has been armed with 81-mm and 107-mm mortars, anti-tank guided missiles, flamethrowers, 20-mm cannon, Vulcan six-barrelled anti-aircraft Gatling gun and even fitted with turrets for tank guns.

Inside the M113

This is an M125, an M113 adapted to carry an 81-mm mortar on a revolving turntable. These proved very useful during the Vietnam war, providing mechanised units with valuable indirect fire capability of their own.

81-mm mortar
This is the M29 mortar, which fires a variety of ammunition with minimum ranges between 46 and 72 metres and maximum ranges of 3800-4500 metres. Sustained rate of fire is four or five rounds per minute.

Tracks
The M113 is fully amphibious and uses its tracks to propel itself through the water at about 5 km/h. The rubber track shroud controls the flow of water over the tracks when swimming.

Mortar ammunition
The M125 can carry up to 114 rounds of ammunition for the 81-mm mortar. There were several instances in Vietnam of M125s being used as normal APCs, still carrying mortar bombs, which had dire consequences if they were penetrated by enemy anti-weapons.

Aluminium armour
The M113's hull is made of aluminium, much lighter than steel but much less effective as armour. The hull is proof against small-arms fire and shell splinters, and M113s proved remarkably tough in Vietnam: only 15 per cent of those hit were permanently knocked out.

In other support roles the M113 continues to be incredibly versatile. It provides all the US Army's mobile air defence: after the humiliating failure of the Sergeant York 40-mm anti-aircraft gun system, the M168 Vulcan soldiers on. This is an M113 fitted with the Navy-modified 20-mm gun with a gyro lead computing sight and a range-determining radar attached. The Army's self-propelled Chapparal surface-to-air missile system is

B Company, 1/50th Infantry, 173rd Airborne Division advance on the village of Phu Loc during a search for local Viet Cong and two enemy nurses in May 1968. Unusually, the M113s still carry prominent US Army markings.

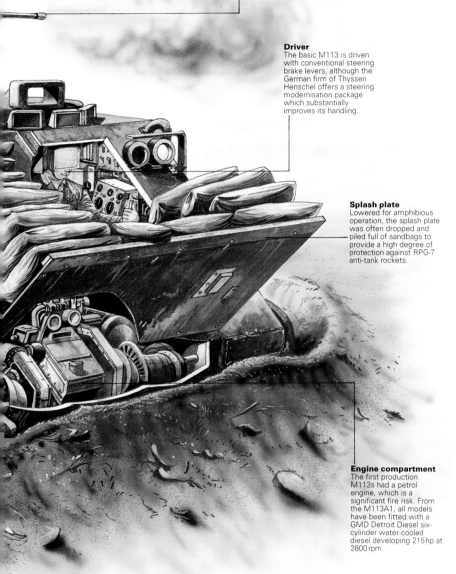

Additional armour
The South Vietnamese experience with M113s in the early 1960s revealed that the machine-gunner was an easy target for enemy infantrymen, and M113s soon sprouted extra armour plate. The back plate is a two-part section overlapped by the large gunshield fitted to the machine-gun.

.50-cal machine-gun
The M125 retains the standard machine gun armament of the M113 APC. This was essential in Vietnam, where convoys were frequently ambushed at very short range.

Driver
The basic M113 is driven with conventional steering brake levers, although the German firm of Thyssen Henschel offers a steering modernisation package which substantially improves its handling.

Splash plate
Lowered for amphibious operation, the splash plate was often dropped and piled full of sandbags to provide a high degree of protection against RPG-7 anti-tank rockets.

Engine compartment
The first production M113s had a petrol engine, which is a significant fire risk. From the M113A1, all models have been fitted with a GMD Detroit Diesel six-cylinder water-cooled diesel developing 215hp at 2800 rpm.

*The **M577** is an M113 with a much higher roof, used as a mobile command post or a medical treatment vehicle. It can carry an external generator to power its communications equipment.*

mounted on the M548 tracked cargo carrier chassis, another development of the ubiquitous M113.

Anti-tank weapon

M113s will continue to provide considerable long-range anti-tank firepower, despite the introduction of the TOW-armed Bradley. The US Army has some 1,400 M113s fitted with TOW anti-tank guided missiles which are launched from a pop-up pedestal that retracts into the troop compartment. The M901 'Improved TOW' vehicle is simply a more capable anti-tank variant with the Emerson ground-launched TOW system in an armoured launcher, and a target acquisition sight mounted on two

arms. Over 2,500 M901s will be in US Army service by the end of the decade.

Less exciting to watch, but of enormous tactical importance, are the M577 series of command post vehicles. By raising the roof behind the driver enough space is created in the troop compartment for a command team to have room to operate; more space can be created by fitting a tent to the back when the vehicle is in a static position. An externally mounted generator provides power for extra radios and associated command equipment. This model of the M113 is also suitable for mobile medical treatment.

To dig fellow members of the M113 family out of trouble, the US Army de-

veloped the M113A2 recovery vehicle. Its hydraulic winch and auxiliary crane enable it to recover vehicles after it has dug spades into the ground to anchor itself firmly. This is a far cry from the Vietnam days, when all manner of ingenious devices were invented to allow basic M113s to trundle around the waterlogged Mekong Delta. Block and tackle systems were fitted to drag APCs over terrain that was too wet to drive over but too dry to use the M113's amphibious ability.

Daisy chain

Thanks to its relatively low ground pressure, the M113 manages fairly well in boggy ground if enough operate together. In the Mekong Delta the 'Daisy Chain' method of linking up to 15 APCs together enabled rice paddies to be crossed successfully.

More recent additions to the M113 family include the M1059 smoke generator, a self-propelled and self-explanatory vehicle of which nearly 200 will soon be in US service. FMC have developed the original vehicle out of all recognition and produced the 'Armoured Infantry Fighting Vehicle', an MICV of strikingly modern appearance and high capability yet costing a fraction of the bill for an M2 Bradley. This is a private venture calculated to win export sales and place another question mark on the Bradley's cost-effectiveness.

Like most NATO forces, the West German army uses the M113, and Thyssen-Henschel have developed a much improved model with modern steering gear. A steering wheel and footbrake replace the traditional steering brake levers and offer many advantages: direction-keeping is more stable through continuous steering and manoeuvrability is dramatically increased.

The Australian army operates 45 M113s fitted with the turret of the British Scorpion reconnaissance vehicle armed with a 76-mm gun. These replace 18 M113s which carried the

Re-supply during the invasion of Cambodia, May 1970: note the armoured back plate for the .50-cal machine-gunner with peace symbol painted on it. The Huey is named 'Beaver's Abortion'.

turret of the old Saladin armoured car. Standard Australian M113s carry a turret with a .30-cal machine-gun and 5,000 rounds of ammunition.

Zeldas

The Israeli army has made wide use of M113s since the late 1960s, when they began to replace the World War II half-tracks still in service with the IDF. When the Israelis invaded Lebanon in 1982 their M113s, called Zeldas, were protected by a thick extra layer of appliqué armour, which helps protect them against the HEAT warheads of RPG-7 rocket launchers, the most widely encountered anti-tank weapon in the Middle East.

Battlefield Evaluation: comparing

M113

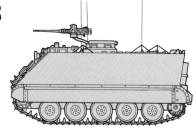

The simplicity of the M113 is one of the reasons for its enormous success. Easily converted to specialist weapons carriers, supply vehicles or command posts, it has even formed the basis for FMC's AIFV, a cost-effective rival for the M2 Bradley. The standard M113 APC has good battlefield mobility, adequate armament and is fully amphibious.

Specification:
Crew: 2+11
Combat weight: 11 tonnes
Road speed: 67 km/h
Power-to-weight ratio: 19 hp/tonne
Length: 4.86 m
Height: 1.82 m
Armament: 1×.50-cal machine-gun

Assessment
Firepower	★★
Protection	★★
Age	★★★★★
Worldwide users	★★★★★

The M113 is the most successful Armoured Personnel Carrier, in service with over 50 different armies.

BTR-60

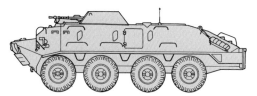

The wheeled BTR-60 and the tracked BTR-50 appeared at about the same time as the M113; the BTR-60 equipped infantry divisions while the BTR-50 was used by the Motor Rifle regiments in Soviet tank divisions. The BTR-60 is substantially cheaper to build and operate than an M113, but it is less mobile, particularly over boggy ground, and not as easy for the infantry section to deploy from.

Specification:
Crew: 2+14
Combat weight: 10.3 tonnes
Road speed: 80 km/h
Power-to-weight ratio: 18 hp/tonne
Length: 7.5 m
Height: 22 m
Armament: 1×14.5-mm and 1×7.62-mm machine-gun

Assessment
Firepower	★★★
Protection	★
Age	★★★★★
Worldwide users	★★★★★

Cheaper but less capable than M113, the BTR-60 series has also proved highly successful.

BTR-50

Built on the chassis of the PT-76 light tank, the BTR-50 can carry nearly twice as many men as the M113 but it is incredibly noisy and kicks up a huge dust cloud in dry weather conditions. It was not as successful as the M113, and from the late 1960s the Soviets began to replace it with the revolutionary BMP.

Specification:
Crew: 2+20
Combat weight: 14 tonnes
Road speed: 44 km/h
Power-to-weight ratio: 17 hp/tonne
Length: 7 m
Height: 2 m
Armament: 1×7.62-mm machine-gun

Assessment
Firepower	★★
Protection	★★
Age	★★★★★
Worldwide users	★★★★

The BTR-50 can cram in up to 20 troops, but has been replaced in the Soviet army.

Twenty-seven years after its introduction, the M113 is more popular than ever. The US Army continues to modernise its vast fleet of M113s, updating powerplant, transmission and performance. New models with stretched crew compartments and various armaments are offered for export, and the Army is studying ways of fitting both active and passive NBC systems and appliqué armour along the lines of the Israeli model.

In Vietnam, where the M113 received its baptism of fire, thousands of vehicles supplied to the South were captured in 1975 and a few 'Green Dragons' continue to serve their new masters.

Apart from its main use as an APC, the M113 serves in many different roles. This M113 has a Hughes TOW anti-tank missile launcher on a retractable pedestal mounting which pops back into the troop compartment when not in use.

the M113 with its rivals

BMP

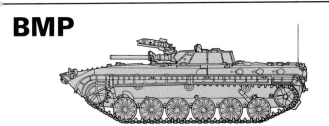

The BMP is designed to allow the infantry section to fight from within the vehicle, and its own heavy armament allows it to join in an assault. Originally the M113 was designed as a traditional APC, simply to ferry the infantry into action but not to fight as a combat vehicle: it is completely outmatched by the BMP, but the latter is far more expensive and designed to fight a very different kind of battle.

Specification:
Crew: 3+8
Combat weight: 13.5 tonnes
Road speed: 80 km/h
Power-to-weight ratio: 22 hp/tonne
Length: 6.74 m
Height: 2.15 m
Armament: 1×73-mm gun; 1×'Sagger' missile launcher; 1×7.62-mm machine-gun

Assessment
Firepower	*****
Protection	**
Age	*****
Worldwide users	*****

This BMP was obtained by the US Army and used for training US personnel in Soviet tactics.

AMX VCI

Developed in the 1950s, the AMX VCI is a simple APC which is not as capable as the M113. Like early models of the American vehicle it has a petrol engine at the front; it has no amphibious capability, and the first production versions had no NBC system. Like the M113, the VCI was used for many different roles including self-propelled mortars and anti-tank missile carriers. It has now been largely replaced by the AMX-10 MICV.

Specification:
Crew: 3+10
Combat weight: 15 tonnes
Road speed: 60 km/h
Power-to-weight ratio: 16.6 hp/tonne
Length: 5.7 m
Height: 2.1 m
Armament: 1×12.7-mm or 7.62-mm machine-gun or 1×20-mm cannon

Assessment
Firepower	**
Protection	**
Age	*****
Worldwide users	**

The AMX VCI is the French equivalent of the M113, now largely replaced by the AMX-10 Infantry Combat Vehicle.

FV 432

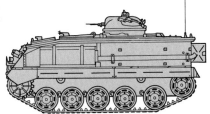

While the USA developed the M113 and ultimately sold it to over 50 nations, the British Army adopted the FV 432 APC. Unlike the M113 it is not amphibious without extensive preparation; it is also heavier and slower, but provides marginally better protection for the occupants. Out of production since 1971, it will soldier on for a long time to come but will be supplemented by MCV-80 from 1988 onwards.

Specification:
Crew: 2+10
Combat weight: 15 tonnes
Road speed: 52 km/h
Power-to-weight ratio: 15.7 hp/tonne
Length: 5.25 m
Height: 1.87 m
Armament: 1×7.62-mm machine-gun

Assessment
Firepower	**
Protection	***
Age	*****
Worldwide users	*

The British Army also developed its own APC, the FV 432, which will continue in service for many years.

T-54/55: Desert Warrior

The T-54 series of Main Battle Tanks has seen more combat than any other type of post-war tank. They rumbled into Prague in 1968 to extinguish Czech hopes of freedom, and they crashed through the gates of the Presidential Palace in Saigon. They have fought in most African and Asian wars since the 1960s, and are still operated in large numbers within the Warsaw Pact and amongst Soviet-supplied forces worldwide.

Although the first T-54s were manufactured 40 years ago, the type is still operational all over the world and various manufacturers are offering conversion deals to completely modernise this veteran tank.

The T-54 series includes a bewildering number of different models. The original production tank was soon altered, and many modifications introduced by subsequent versions were applied retrospectively, so it can be difficult to tell them apart.

Early model T-54s were very basic, World War II-style tanks but had a very powerful armament for their time. The low turret presented an impressively small silhouette to the enemy, but only by cramming the commander, gunner and loader into an incredibly small space. The gunner and commander are squashed together on the left of the gun while the loader sits to its right.

Three shells are positioned in a rack in the turret rear, and the loader has to twist round and load them into the

With its light weight and low profile, the T-55 can still be an effective tank if fitted with a modern gun and fire control system. This Egyptian vehicle carries an L7 105-mm gun and two banks of British smoke dischargers. The Soviet 12.7-mm machine-gun has been removed from its mount above the loader's hatch.

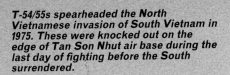

T-55 in its 'natural environment', the snow-covered central USSR. Widely used in the Middle East, the T-55 was designed as a result of Soviet experience in World War II and was not intended for desert operations.

breech with his left hand. They weigh 25 kg each, but his problems begin when these three have been fired because the T-54s and early T-55s have no turret floor. When the turret rotates, the gun breech moves round but you do not, unless you are sitting in your seat which hangs from the turret roof. If you are standing, you can be crushed by the breech.

The T-54/55's main armament is the D-10T 100-mm rifled gun, a mighty

This T-55 has been fitted with a British L7 105-mm gun instead of the old Soviet 100-mm weapon as part of a modernisation package offered by Royal Ordnance.

T-54/55s spearheaded the North Vietnamese invasion of South Vietnam in 1975. These were knocked out on the edge of Tan Son Nhut air base during the last day of fighting before the South surrendered.

piece for its time but inadequate for the 1980s. The AP and HVAPDS-T ammunition for the D-10 lacks the penetration to destroy the latest generation of NATO armour except at very close range, and its HEAT round is equally ineffective. Against M48s, Leopard 1s and other lightly protected AFVs it will do the job, but the 15-20 seconds needed to reload would cost it dearly in action against most NATO tanks with a competent crew.

Dangerous engine

The engines on Soviet-built T-54/55s are often so badly made that they self-destruct: oil lines are easily blocked by a mass of loose metal filings and the engine overheats and catches fire. Made of magnesium alloy, it burns nicely and the whole tank can easily be destroyed. Some Warsaw Pact armies used to take the precaution of rebuilding the engines

Inside the T-55

Laser rangefind...
The weaknesses c...
100-mm gun were
exacerbated on m...
versions of the T-5...
a primitive fire con...
system. The Sovie...
no sign of re-armir...
T-55s, but the add...
laser rangefinder g...
increases the effe...
range of the 100-m...

Driver
The T-54/55 is a very uncomfortable vehicle to drive; double clutching to change gear and a dreadful suspension system make it an exhausting experience. The T-55s offered for sale by Israel have a much improved driver's station with steering wheel, new transmission and a decent suspension.

in T-54/55s they had bought, or, better still, manufacturing the engines themselves.

The T-54 was succeeded by the T-54A, B and C, each adding marginal improvements. The gun received a bore-evacuator, power elevation and both vertical and horizontal stabilisation: other changes included infra-red night vision equipment, automatic fire-extinguishers and an air filter.

T-55 introduction

The T-55 was first observed in the 1961 November Parade and introduced a more powerful engine, better transmission, a turret basket and nine more rounds of ammunition. Two years later, production switched to the T-55A, which featured an anti-radiation lining and an NBC system to protect the crew from nuclear fallout. This became the most numerically important model of the series, and many of its features were retrofitted to earlier tanks. The most significant improvement noted in recent years is a laser rangefinder, which began to appear on Warsaw Pact T-54/55s in the late 1970s.

Even with all these improvements, why is the T-54/55 still in such widespread service and important enough to warrant the expense of laser rangefinders? It remains a crude and simple combat vehicle harking back to World War II rather than looking forward to the 21st century.

Failure of T-62

One answer is that its replacement, the T-62, failed to live up to expectation: it is estimated that the T-62 cost about three times the price of a T-54/55 and it certainly did not provide triple value. Its armour protection is very similar, and its weight and battlefield mobility are also little different. The most significant change was the adoption of the 115-mm smoothbore gun which, although capable of destroying Western tanks at longer ranges, probably did not offer a wide enough margin to satisfy its critics. For these reasons the USSR

This Syrian T-55 was knocked out on the Golan Heights during the 1973 Arab-Israeli war. Syrian numerical advantage was nullified by inflexible tactics, poor gunnery and lack of co-ordination.

continued to manufacture the tried and tested T-55 until 1981, a long time after it abandoned T-62 production.

China has copied the T-54 and produced one of the worst tanks inflicted on an army since 1945. Designated the T-59, the workmanship is appalling and it incorporates few of the improvements effected to the T-54/55s in Warsaw Pact service. The gun is not stabilised, so firing on the move is simply wasting ammunition; the choice of ammunition is more limited, and this is as badly manufactured as the rest of the tank.

The Pakistani army was supplied with large numbers of T-59s and has been trying to rectify its shortcomings for many years. Ironically, their Indian opponents in the 1971 war used T-55s.

The Israeli army captured large numbers of T-54/55s in 1967 when the ill-starred Egyptian advance into the Sinai desert was decisively defeated. Many T-54/55s had broken down and were baking in the sun, waiting to be taken back for repair, when the Israelis overran them. Beggars can't be choosers, and the Israelis pressed them into service and used an entire brigade of them in the 1973 Yom Kippur war. That conflict netted another large haul of T-54/55s which were

Hull front armour
This is 97mm thick, sloped at 58° on the top part, and 99mm thick on the lower part. The hull sides are protected by 79mm at 0° and the rear is just 46mm thick.

East German T-54 training tanks in operation. Like many Warsaw Pact forces, the East German army continued to rely on the T-54/55 rather than convert entirely to the T-62. First-line units are now equipped with T-72s, but T-54/55s still equip second-line and training formations.

T-54/55: Desert Warrior

This is the final production version of the T-55 with 'live' track, a laser rangefinder and radiation covers. Manufacture at the Omsk tank factory did not cease until 1981, and after 40 years in production about 50,000 are believed to have been manufactured in the USSR. When Chinese and Warsaw Pact production figures are added, the total number of T-54/55s built is near 100,000. Compare this with the production totals for its American contemporary, the M48 (11,703) or the British Centurion (4,423).

Gunner
By modern standards, the armour-piercing shell from the T-54/55's 100-mm gun is severely lacking in penetrative power and its more lethal HEAT round is inaccurate. Worse, it takes 15-20 seconds to reload, since the gun must be fully elevated to give the loader room to extract the empty case and load a fresh round.

Commander
The commander has a cupola which can be traversed through 360° independently of the turret. On the Israeli-rebuilt T-55s the cupola is lowered flush with the turret.

7-mm anti-aircraft machine-gun
appeared on later versions of the T-54 and is ed to many of the 4/55 variants.

TPK-1 sight
This gives the commander reasonable visibility out to 400 metres at night. The gunner's sights function out to about 800 metres.

Turret armour
The front of the turret is protected by 203 mm of armour and the sides by 150 mm. This relatively thick armour combined with its low silhouette makes the T-54/55 well protected for a tank weighing only 36 tonnes.

Loader
Only three rounds are stored in the turret, after which the loader must leave his seat to collect shells from the hull. T-54s and early T-55s had no turret floor, so if the turret rotated and the loader was standing on the hull floor he could be crushed by the breech.

Tracks
T-54/55s have Christie-type torsion bar suspension with five large road wheels. A useful recognition feature is the gap between the first and second wheels. The last production model shown here has 'live' track, but all previous versions had 'dead' (not under tension) track which hung loosely and sometimes led to the tank shedding its track.

also modified for use against their former owners.

The Israelis extensively improved their T-54/55s by replacing the obsolete 100-mm gun with the L7 105-mm weapon widely used in NATO, fitting a modern fire control system, new night vision aids and American machine-guns. From the point of view of the crew, the most popular improvement was the installation of air conditioning: a vital feature of a tank intended for desert warfare.

In the last few years Israel has offered modernised T-54/55s for export – tanks that bear little relation to the poorly made and badly maintained specimens originally acquired from the Arabs. Now powered by American General Motors' engines with completely new transmission, they have a completely revised driver's station with a steering wheel

instead of sticks and a good suspension system.

In the UK, Royal Ordnance has developed for the T-54/55 an update kit which centres around the replacement of the 100-mm gun with a British

Victorious Chadian soldiers pose beside Libyan T-55s captured in April 1987 at Faya Largeau. Note the driver's hatches swung open and the emptied stowage containers on the turret sides.

105-mm weapon. This is specially aimed at the Egyptians and Pakistanis, who are keen to modernise their tank fleets. Egypt has also signed a deal with the American company, Teledyne, to bring their T-54/55s up to the Israeli standard.

Ageing vehicles

By the age of 40, most tanks are well into old age and are only fit for parades in African capitals. The T-54/55 was produced on a phenomenal scale; probably over 100,000 were manufactured, and the owners have a strong incentive to spin out the lives of these ageing vehicles. In several cases, notably Egypt and Pakistan, they form

A T-54 of the North Vietnamese Army makes history by entering the Presidential Palace in Saigon. NVA tanks had a terrible effect on the already shaky morale of the South Vietnamese soldiers.

Battlefield Evaluation: comparing

T-54/55

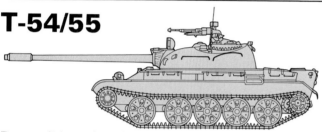

The most widely manufactured tank since World War II, the T-54/55 has seen action all over the world and remains in widespread service despite its age. The T-54/55 is light but reasonably armoured and easier to maintain than more recent NATO or Soviet tanks. On the other hand, it has the familiar weaknesses of Soviet armour: no concessions to crew comfort, limited depression of the main armament and a primitive fire control system.

Specification: (T-55)
Crew: 4
Combat weight: 36 tonnes
Road speed: 50km/h
Power to weight ratio: 16hp/tonne
Length: 6.45m
Height: 2.4m
Armament: 1×100-mm gun; 1×7.62-mm machine-gun plus optional 12.7-mm AA machine-gun

Assessment
Firepower ★★★
Protection ★★★★
Age ★★★★★
Worldwide users ★★★★★

A re-armed T-55: few other tanks can boast as long a combat record as the T-54/55 series.

M48

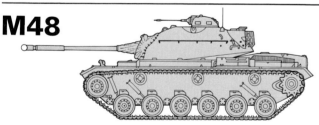

The American M48 is substantially less well armoured than the T-54/55 despite being nearly 10 tonnes heavier. On the other hand, it carries 60 rounds of ammunition for its main armament, whereas the T-54/55 only carries 44. Overall standards of finish are vastly superior: the engines are much better built, being more reliable and giving a better power-to-weight ratio despite the heavier weight. Israeli M48s defeated Arab T-54/55s in 1967 but this says more about the soldiers than the vehicles involved.

Specification:
Crew: 4
Combat weight: 45 tonnes
Road speed: 42km/h
Power to weight ratio: 18hp/tonne
Length: 6.7m
Height: 3.1m
Armament: 1×90-mm gun; 1×12.7-mm and 1.62-mm machine guns

Assessment
Firepower ★★★
Protection ★★★
Age ★★★★★
Worldwide users ★★★

The T-54 followed Soviet wartime experience, but the M48 was built in the mediocre tradition of the Sherman.

M47

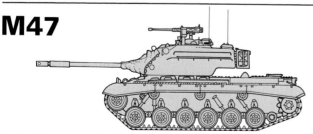

As the US Army adopted the M48 it discarded the M47s built during the early 1950s, and many of these were supplied to US Allies. Armour protection is similar to that of the M48 – rather weaker than that of the T-54/55. The 90-mm gun is broadly equivalent in hitting power to the Soviet 100-mm rifled gun, but M47s have no NBC defence. Variously modified versions of the M47 continue to serve throughout southern Europe from Spain to Turkey.

Specification:
Crew: 5
Combat weight: 46 tonnes
Road speed: 48km/h
Power to weight ratio: 17.5hp/tonne
Length: 6.35m
Height: 3m
Armament: 1×90-mm gun; 1×12.7-mm and 1×7.62-mm machine-guns

Assessment
Firepower ★★★
Protection ★★★
Age ★★★★★
Worldwide users ★★★

The US Army never fully adopted the M47 but it was widely exported to American allies.

a major proportion of the army's tank strength, and modernisation is cheaper than buying new replacements.

The new generation of NATO armour – M1 Abrams, Leopard 2 and Challenger – are so cripplingly expensive that, outside the Alliance, only countries like Saudi Arabia can afford them; and the vehicles they replace, M60s, Leopard 1s and Chieftains, are unlikely to appear on the export market in major numbers. In the Warsaw Pact, many armies never fully adopted the T-62 and units equipped with T-54/55s are moving directly to the T-72, their veteran tanks finally passing into reserve.

Egyptian T-55s come ashore from American landing craft during joint exercises near Alexandria. Like most post-war Soviet tanks, the T-55 can schnorkel across rivers after a great deal of preparation.

the T-54/55 with its rivals

Centurion

The Centurion appeared before the T-54 and is the only tank which can boast a longer service life. Substantially heavier and correspondingly slower, the Centurion is no better armoured than the T-54, but later models with their 105-mm guns were much more effective in action. Israeli Centurions have been much improved, and consistently defeated T-54/55 series tanks. In 1970 Jordanian Centurions decisively beat a force of Syrian T-54/55s. The South African Army continues to use about 300 Centurions.

Specification: (Mk 13)
Crew: 4
Combat weight: 52 tonnes
Road speed: 35 km/h
Power to weight ratio: 12.5hp/tonne
Length: 7.8 m
Height: 3 m
Armament: 1×12.7-mm ranging machine-gun; 2×7.62-mm machine-guns

Assessment
Firepower ★★★★
Protection ★★★★
Age ★★★★★
Worldwide users ★★

Once the Israelis had taken it in hand, the British Centurion was a far better tank than the T-55.

T-10

In the 1950s the major powers continued to produce heavy tanks: the British produced the 65-tonne Conqueror and the Americans deployed the M103, which they perversely gave to the Marines. The Soviets introduced the T-10 to replace their World War II JS IIs and JSIIIs. T-10s were never exported and served in independent heavy tank battalions attached to tank armies. They went out of service sometime during the 1970s and no new heavy tanks were built.

Specification:
Crew: 4
Combat weight: 52 tonnes
Road speed: 42 km/h
Power to weight ratio: unknown
Length: 7 m
Height: 2.25 m
Armament: 1×122-mm gun; 1×12.7-mm or 14.5-mm AA machine-gun; 1×7.62-mm machine-gun

Assessment
Firepower ★★★
Protection ★★★★★
Age ★★★★★
Worldwide users ★

The T-10 replaced the JS III as the last of the monstrous Soviet heavy tanks.

T-34

Widely rated as the finest tank produced during World War II, the T-34's career continues. The Soviets still manufacture 85-mm tank gun ammunition and maintain T-34s in mothballs for export to African allies like Angola. Unlike the 1939-45 models, the T-34s encountered by South African troops in Angola often have T-55-style road wheels, better engines and infra-red night vision devices. The T-34 was the ultimate soldier-proof tank and its use as a bush tank makes a great deal of sense (unless your enemy is equipped with modern armour). European mercenaries found it difficult to knock out T-34s with 66-mm LAWs during the Angolan civil war of 1976.

Specification:
Crew: 4 (5 if bow machine-gun retained)
Combat weight: 32 tonnes
Road speed: 55 km/h
Power to weight ratio: 15.6hp/tonne
Length: 6.19 m
Height: 2.7 m
Armament: 1×85-mm gun; 2×7.62-mm machine-guns

Assessment
Firepower ★★
Protection ★★★
Age ★★★★★
Worldwide users ★★★

The T-34 continues to see action in Africa, particularly in Angola against UNITA rebels.

Trapping Animals for Food

Meat is the most nourishing food for man, and is certainly the most satisfying for the fugitive who is surviving for any length of time in the wild. Collecting and eating grubs may be an easier option than trapping larger animals, but you have to get through a lot of worms and caterpillars to beat a decent rabbit or duck. Here we describe how to set about catching whatever you find.

The first thing to know is that all animals are edible (but not necessary the whole of the beast). The second thing is that they're nearly all very difficult to catch and you'll have to use all your skills to be successful; and that means understanding the animal's way of life.

Daily habits

They're usually fairly regular in their habits, using the same paths and trails, drinking at the same places on the river bank and from pools, sleeping in the same sheltered places. They also have a timetable, and stick to it; if an animal went to a certain place to drink at dawn this morning, there's a very good chance that it will do the same again tomorrow. Spend time looking for signs of animals.

If there's a lot of animal activity going on, find a hiding place and stay in it until you recognise the local wildlife patterns. It will make trap-

Small animals make their homes in all sorts of unlikely places. Sheets of old corrugated iron like this one will often be home to a family of mice – but snakes find it comfortable here too, so lift the edge with a knife or a piece of wood – not with your hand.

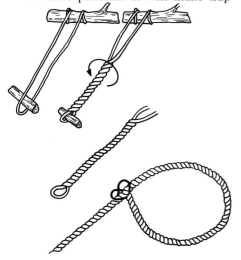

A simple wire snare
The simplest snare of all is just a running noose, but you can improve on that by making it out of a pair of wires twisted together. The two loops of single wire that make the 'slip knot' will lock into the twists and stop the animal getting away.

ping or hunting them a great deal easier. All you've got going for you is your intelligence; they've lived there all their lives!

Unless you have an accurate weapon, such as a rifle, shotgun or cross-bow, hunting will be a lot less likely to provide you with dinner than trapping. In a hostile environment, where there are enemy forces or natives, hunting is almost certain to be impossible anyway, but let's look at some of the basic skills you'll need to hunt game in the wild.

Always assume that any small animals in the area will be wary and quick to run away. If they spot you,

hear you or smell you (remember that their sense of smell may be a thousand times better than yours), they will either go to ground or disappear off into the distance. Seeing them before they become aware of you greatly increases your chances of catching them.

They often use the same pathways and drinking places, and make perma-

Setting a Snare

A snare has two essential parts – the wire noose and the stick to anchor it into the ground. This is how to put it to use.

1. The snare itself is just a running noose of wire with a tail of strong string.

2. A branch of a Christmas tree is ideal for the peg of a snare. Trim off both ends.

4. Pass the tail through the slot, make two turns around the stalk and tie it off.

5. Anchor the stick into the ground so that the snare is a hand's breadth above the ground.

3. Cut a slit in one end to take the string tail.

6. Set your snare along tracks and paths used by animals. This track has been beaten down by rabbits and is an ideal spot.

---

nent homes. Look for their signs – tracks, paths in grass, faeces, dens, feeding places – and use that intelligence to help you set up a plan to catch them.

Camouflage and approach

Remember, the fieldcraft that makes you a good foot-soldier can also make you a good hunter. Always obey the rules of camouflage and approach. Never silhouette yourself against the skyline, even in woodland. Always move upwind or across wind. Approach streams, rivers and waterholes very carefully, especially around dawn and dusk. Find cover and get into it, and wait for the animals.

And stay still! Fidgetting may cost you a meal – and that may end up costing you your life.

A pole to catch squirrels
Take a pole, fix some wire snares to it and lean it up against a tree where you've seen squirrels. It may seem too simple to be true, but these inquisitive creatures are quite likely to get caught up before too long.

Siting traps
You can't just put a trap anywhere and expect it to work. Careful siting is the most important part of trapping. The mouths of burrows are good places, but you must be sure to disguise or obliterate your scent.

Deadfalls

The figure-four deadfall is simple to make and surprisingly sensitive. The props should be as thin as you can make them, the fall itself as heavy as possible. The one shown here is relatively small, but you can make larger ones too, to stun larger animals.

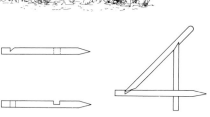

Cut two sticks of roughly equal length, and trim and notch them as shown. Sharpen one end of each stick, one to go into the ground and the other to take the bait.

Cut and notch a third, longer stick to form the third side of the triangle.

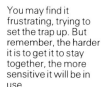

Pay careful attention to the notches. Cut them too shallow and they won't hold for very long.

You may find it frustrating, trying to set the trap up. But remember, the harder it is to get it to stay together, the more sensitive it will be in use.

Larger game, even if it sees you, may not take flight straight away. Stop and keep still until it loses interest, and then approach in a wide zig-zag. In hills and mountains, always try to get above the animal you're stalking.

Best target areas

If you are shooting game, the best targets are the head, neck and the spine just behind the shoulder. Take your time, and make the first shot count – because you're not likely to get a second chance. If you hit and wound the animal and it runs off, follow the blood trail. A badly wounded creature won't have the strength to run far. Give it the chance to go to ground before following it up. Approach slowly and then make the kill. Don't waste ammunition if you can finish it off by clubbing it.

Hunting, however, should take second place to making and setting traps. Traps are much more likely to provide you with a lasting supply of meat. Simple ones are very easy to make and set: the simplest of all is a snare – a slip noose firmly pegged into the ground or anchored to a rock or tree. Make them from wire if it's available, or use plastic fishing line, string or even line made up from natural fibres.

These snares are especially effective when you set them at the entrance to burrows and dens. Set them in trees to catch squirrels, or make a 'squirrel pole': an eight- to 12-ft pole with perhaps half-a-dozen snares around it, leaned up against a tree used by squirrels. It may sound too easy, but squirrels are inquisitive creatures and will often investigate something new just for the fun of it.

You're not likely to be able to kill anything larger than a rabbit or a small cat with a wire snare, though you may slow down larger animals so that you have a better chance of clubbing them to death.

Looking for signs

Trapping, even more than hunting, depends on how well you can read the signs. There is no point in placing a trap just anywhere hoping that an animal will stumble into it by chance! Entrances to burrows and tunnels are the best place. Look for signs that they are occupied – fresh droppings, signs of feeding and movement in and out.

Unless you're using wire for the snare, which may stand up on its own, you will have to make a stand to hold the noose open. Two twigs, one each side of the mouth of the burrow or the path will do, with another one perhaps placed across the top to support the trap.

Human scent

Don't forget to cover your scent, both on the snare itself and on the surrounding ground: soaking the snare in a stream after you've made it and before setting it is one way. Or you can rub it with cold ashes, or disguise your own scent with something stronger – urine from the bladder of a dead animal, for example. Animals are usually attracted to urine from their own kind.

Improved noose

You can improve on the simple noose, and make it more difficult for the animal to escape from the trap, by inter-twining two lengths of wire. Use the two strands that are left at the end to make up a double running loop. These two loops will naturally catch in the twists of the wire that makes the body of the line and noose, and will make it much more difficult for the animal to wriggle out of the noose.

You can always let predators do your hunting for you. Watch until you can work out their pattern of activity, then wait for them to make a kill. If you rush them you'll often cause them to drop their prey.

Hanging snares

Hanging snares are a more secure way of holding on to the animal that you've caught. They use the creature's own weight to keep it from wriggling out of the noose. Apart from the wire noose itself, to make a hanging snare you need a sapling close to the run you've chosen, and a forked stick, or one bent over into a hoop.

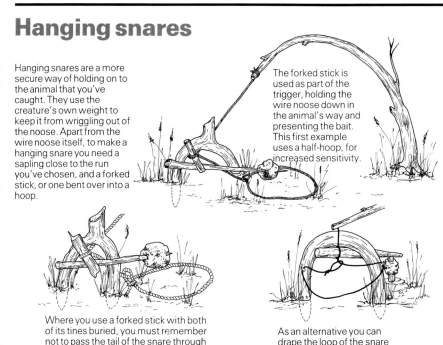

The forked stick is used as part of the trigger, holding the wire noose down in the animal's way and presenting the bait. This first example uses a half-hoop, for increased sensitivity.

Where you use a forked stick with both of its tines buried, you must remember not to pass the tail of the snare through the hoop. The toggle that holds the baited trigger is caught in a loop of the tail, not knotted.

As an alternative you can drape the loop of the snare right around the hoop. This gets the noose off the ground without needing extra sticks.

Skinning a Rabbit

All furry animals have to be skinned before you can cook them. Here's how to deal with small creatures such as rabbits or squirrels.

1. Lay the animal down on its back, spread all four legs wide, and cut from the anus up to the breastbone, taking care not to rupture the intestine.

2. Cut the skin through around all four paws at the first joint. Remove the guts, starting from the throat and working downwards. Do not eat these innards.

3. Now you can peel the skin off. You may find it necessary to remove the tail first.

4. Take the skin off in one piece. A firm grip and a quick pull are all that is needed.

5. The last thing to do is to remove the head. Keep the skin for making clothing.

You can even scare off large animals this way – cats and bears, for instance. Building a fire when you've frightened them off will often make them stay away long enough for them to forget you've robbed them of their meal. But unless you're well armed, don't be too ready to take on these large predators yourself.

Obvious targets

Don't go around chasing squirrels while ignoring more obvious targets such as cows, sheep and other domestic animals – including cats and dogs. They're all food, and often they're just standing around waiting to become somebody's meal – it may as well be yours. Bats and mice make good eating, but do not eat any of their innards, and immediately discard their heads, skin, feet and tails.

In later sections we'll be looking at ways of cooking and preserving meat and fish and – more important for health reasons – ways of spotting the tell-tale signs that flesh is inedible as a result of decay, and what to do if you do eat it! Remember, survival is to do with common sense and intelligence – not with taking chances.

Treadle-spring snare

For really large game you need a bigger noose, but to keep it in the most effective position you will have to make up the much more complex treadle-spring snare.

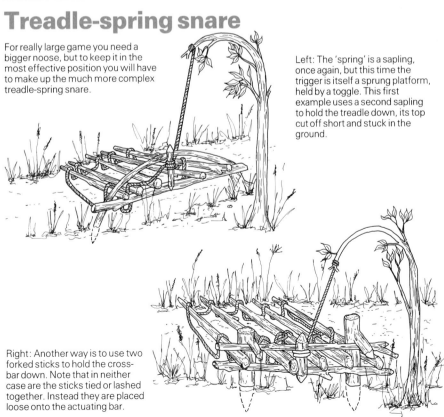

Left: The 'spring' is a sapling, once again, but this time the trigger is itself a sprung platform, held by a toggle. This first example uses a second sapling to hold the treadle down, its top cut off short and stuck in the ground.

Right: Another way is to use two forked sticks to hold the cross-bar down. Note that in neither case are the sticks tied or lashed together. Instead they are placed loose onto the actuating bar.

Survival

Fishing for Food

Fish can see what is on the river bank, although it is a very distorted image. Sudden movement will alert any potential prey, so the key is selecting the right site to spear from and then having the patience not to move until the moment of strike.

The fishing spear has a detachable head secured with twine to the shaft of the spear. The violent movement of the fish is not transferred to the spear shaft, so you can maintain a firm grip of the prey without it wriggling off the spear point.

At a casual glance you might mistake the motionless form on the riverbank for that of someone basking in the sunshine. But the survivor is hard at work, his intent gaze piercing the water surface, searching for the sleek silver shimmer of his next meal.

If you are fortunate enough to be stranded in an area with a lake or river, you have a rich source of food waiting to be gathered. Fish are rich in protein, the brains and skin are rich in fat, and the meat can also be stored long term. The problem is how to remove the fish from his natural environment to yours.

As someone intent purely on survival, you cannot afford any sporting niceties. The fishing techniques you will need to use are usually outlawed. You must be able to catch your fish in quantity, and as easily as possible. Before you actually start fishing remind yourself of the danger of water, especially in your weakened physical state. Should you fall in, remember the tip of the old salmon fishermen –

throw your arms out, crucifix-fashion, and try to float down to a shallow pool where you can wade out. If you panic and throw your arms up in the air you will only sink faster. (In crocodile-infested waters try to stay as dry as possible!)

While fish may seem more easily trapped and hunted than other animals, you must bear in mind that you need to catch an awful lot of fish to provide the same volume of food as a medium-sized land animal. At the end of the day, your catch must be big enough to justify the time and effort. This will be largely dependent on how well stocked your river is.

Catching fish

Whether you decide to hunt or trap fish, the time-honoured hunting rules apply. Study the fish in your locality, see where the biggest fish prefer to swim as the position of the sun changes, get to know their habits – especially their feeding habits. Once you have caught a fish, study its stomach contents to find out what it

Detachable fishing spear heads: note that both have barbs to prevent them being shaken out by the fish. Both have been carved from wood and bound with twine sealed in gum.

was feeding on. The more you know, the easier your task will be.

Hunting fish

Although hunting fish usually produces a smaller catch than trapping them, it can be a quick way to a short term meal, and is ideally suited to survivors on the move. The hunting tools are also simpler and more easily made than trapping gear.

Fish are able to detect unusual disturbances in the water, and can see movement above the water. To avoid alerting them to your presence, always try to minimise your movement and noise. Walk carefully – fish can feel heavy footfalls through the water.

1 Tickling

Some fish, particularly trout and salmon, will allow you to touch them while in the water. To catch fish like this you need to be actually in the water. The ideal type of stream is wide, and shallow and clear.

Approach your fish slowly and carefully, with your hands already in the water. Once you are close enough to touch the fish, pass your upturned hands under him very gently. You will probably fail the first time you do this, out of sheer astonishment, for the fish seem to nestle against your hands. Once your hands are in position, grab the fish. Bend him in your hands and he won't slip away. In one smooth action, cast him onto the bank. While this technique does require the confidence that comes with practice, it does work, and can be a very effective way to catch fish in the right circumstances.

2 Torch and blade

At night, fish can be attracted to light. Wade into a shallow stream with a torch made of birch bark, and you should be able to catch the fish attracted by slashing at them with the blunt end of a machete or a thin blade carved of wood. Make certain you hold the torch high in front of you so as to avoid casting your shadow on the water.

If the river is too deep to wade into, you can use the same technique from the river bank, using a long spear to catch the fish.

Fish maze trap and basket trap

The maze trap

The trap is made up of wooden staves hammered into the river bed with a supporting line connecting the tops of each stave. The trap takes some time to build, but is very effective. The collecting arm should cover the main flow of the river so that the majority of fish swimming upstream are directed into the trap. Each stave should be at least 2 cm thick.

river bank · securing twine · flow

staves

river bed

collecting arm

river

plan view of the trap

The basket trap

This fish trap is made up of wooden staves bound together to form a telescoping basket. In the faster-flowing parts of the river the fish swims into it but cannot turn round to get out, and finds itself beached at the end of the trap.

water level · mouth of trap · basket

direction of flow

twine

supporting poles

river bed

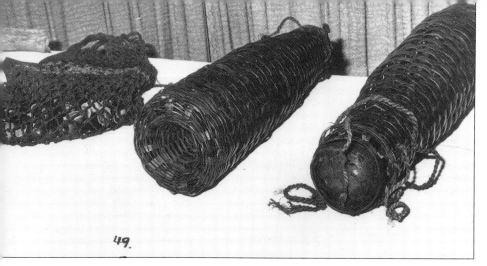

49.

3 Spear and lure

You can easily make fish spears from available wood, and they can be very effective. They fall into two basic categories – pin, and snag. You use the simplest spears to pin the fish to the river bed. They are usually made of a single piece of wood, pronged or split at the point, and crudely barbed. They are very quickly made and very effective.

The 'snag' or 'leister' spears are

These fish traps helped sustain Shoichi Yokoi, a sergeant of the Imperial Japanese army, hiding in the jungles of Guam for 28 years after World War II had ended.

more complicated to make. They work by snagging the fish on barbs rather than pinning the fish to the bottom. For this reason they are better than pin spears in deep water. You can make these spears have detachable heads attached to the spear shaft

by a length of strong cordage. In this way the fish can thrash around without any risk of breaking the spear head.

Spears are best used in conjunction with a suitable lure. Simply carve a small fish-shaped piece of wood, modelled on the local 'small fry', and attach it to a long length of cordage. By drawing this along in the water you should be able to attract the attention of a large predatory fish and 'lure' it within range of your spear. Because water refracts light you will need to aim slightly below where the target appears to be.

4 Line and hook

While you can improvise a line and hook from natural materials, these are best used as 'static traps'. But if you have a survival fishing kit, especially one containing spinners, you will be able to cast your fish. If you don't have any spinners you can improvise them with coins or discarded canned-drink ring-pulls, in fact anything flat and shiny.

Hooks and lines

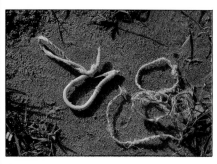

A gorge hook is made from a length of wood bent into shape by steaming and then binding a shaped point to one end. These are excellent hooks for set lines.

A trout caught on a set line and gorge hook. Set lines are a practical way to catch fish if you are going to be near a river for some time. Tie several baited hooks on a line and tie the line to a branch overhanging the river.

Trapping fish

Methods of trapping fish are more useful to you in the long run as they free you to work on your other important chores. However, the apparatus you need will take longer to make. If you are establishing your survival camp, setting fish traps should be one of your priorities. Your land traps will usually take less effort to set and can be more easily tuned to full effectiveness.

1 Maze traps

These are the simplest traps you can construct. They are simply holding pens, which fish can enter easily but cannot leave because of the design of the entrance. When you make this type of trap, make sure that the stakes are securely hammered into the stream bed with a stone maul. Lash the tops of the stakes with cordage – your trap has the constant flow of the river to contend with.

2 Basket traps

Basket traps are slightly more complicated to make than maze traps, but have the advantage that you can carry them easily to wherever there are the most fish. Place the basket so that the river current flows into the basket entrance and raise the downstream end out of the water. Secure the basket with rock or slim willow branches. If you have time you can also construct a funnel of stakes to lead the fish into the basket.

3 Nets

Nets are the hardest fishing aids of all to make, requiring great lengths of

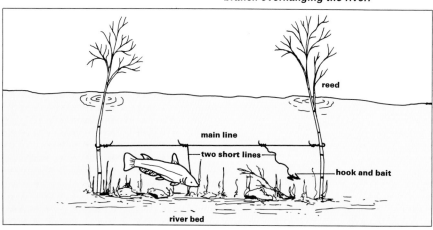

You may not want to risk using a set line in an evasion situation, but you can use the above set line, known as a stakeout. This is a fishing device you can use secretly by setting a line in darkness between two reeds or similar with lines and hooks attached. Check the line at two-hour intervals until dawn, and then remove.

Fish trap in stream

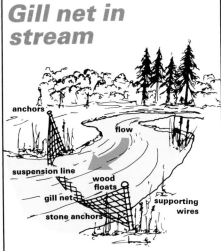

supporting wires

anchors

fish basket or net

flow

rock dyke

Fish traps can be used for freshwater and saltwater fish. There are very effective but takes a good deal of effort to make, and are difficult to carry if you decide to move on.

Gill net in stream

anchors

flow

suspension line

wood floats

gill net

supporting wires

stone anchors

The gill net is perhaps the best way to catch fish, but again it takes time to make it. Stones are used to anchor the bottom of the net and wood floats are set along the top. The net is set at an angle across the river from a suspension line between two suitable anchors.

cordage. Unless you have nylon cord to unravel for netting material or a gill net in your survival kit, this method of trapping is an unrealistic proposition.

If you do have a net set it across a straight section of river. If the river is shallow, place the net at an angle in the water. When you have one, a net is a first rate piece of fishing equipment.

Hook and line

If you have them, fish hooks and line can be used in an endless variety of ways. The easiest and most effective set-up is to set a fixed line across the river and suspend hooks from it at different depths. In this way you can fish several different levels of the river

at the same time.

Always make absolutely certain that your hooks are tied on securely – your life may depend upon them.

Improvising hook and line

In the wild, on your own, you may not be lucky enough to have any hooks or line. But you can improvise them from natural materials.

The simplest improvised hook is the 'gorge' or 'toggle' hook. For this you will need a piece of bone or fire-hardened hardwood. Sharpen this at both ends and secure your line to its middle. When this is baited and taken by the fish it toggles inside the fish's throat, lodging tight. Thorns can also be turned into improvised hooks, and you might even carve a standing hook from a piece of bone.

Fishing line is far more difficult to improvise than a fish hook. The strongest line you are likely to be able to make is a very thin rawhide line. Although rawhide loses much of its

Casting a line. Watch where the fish are rising: that is where the line should go. In a river, fish gather in the pools in the deep calm water, at the bottom of small rapids, at the tail of a pool.

strength when wet, it is still appreciably stronger than most of the plant fibres you will have available. Simply cut a piece of rawhide in a spiral until you have a long thin fishing line. Soak the line before use and don't leave it submerged more than a day or two.

Of the plant fibres you can use, nettle fibres are among the best. But, as with all plant cordage, you will need to gather a lot of nettles, and the process of turning them into cord is slow and laborious. Gather the longest nettles you can find and lay them out to dry in the sun. Once dry, they will have lost their sting and can be handled more easily. Take a mallet and split the stems, remove the pith until only the fibres remain. These can then be rolled on your thigh to produce strong cordage.

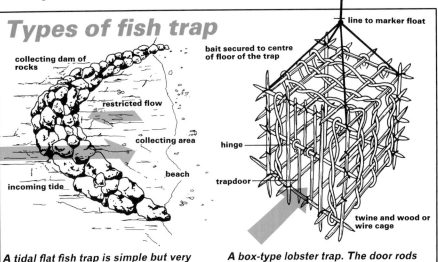

Types of fish trap

collecting dam of rocks

restricted flow

collecting area

beach

incoming tide

bait secured to centre of floor of the trap

line to marker float

hinge

trapdoor

twine and wood or wire cage

A tidal flat fish trap is simple but very laborious to construct. Pick the location at high tide and construct during low tide. You can simply dam existing rocking pools.

A box-type lobster trap. The door rods should be hinged so that they drop behind the lobster after it enters. Bait and sink in three to 10 metres of water.

Survival

Preserving Food in the Wild

To survive in the wilderness you have to become a predator – and that means you have to compete with other, animal predators for the same prey. You can learn a lot about survival by watching the animals around you. Notice how the animal that makes the kill isn't always the one who enjoys the meal.

You can turn this to your advantage, but you also have to protect your kill from being stolen by other animals – not all of them friendly. You need to protect your food from the hordes of bugs and flies that want to eat your food and, worse, lay their eggs in it.

Preserving food is a vitally important skill if you are to survive away from civilisation for a long time. It requires some knowledge and not a little practice to acquire confidence in your own preserved food, but it is well worth the effort. Here is a 'smudge fire', which gently wafts smoke under drying meat or fish. This does not smoke the meat; it simply accelerates the drying process and keeps the flies off while the skin hardens.

With care and the right techniques you should be able to keep your kill at least for long enough to let you eat all of it safely. With practice, you can even preserve your food indefinitely.

Preserving meat

First decide whether or not you intend to hunt large game. Preserving a large animal such as a deer will require considerably greater effort than will preserving a rabbit. The deciding factor is how long you expect to be stranded. If it's likely to be a long time, killing a large animal means less hunting and brings with it a large and useful skin. But it also involves hard work to preserve the meat. Until you become expert at preserving meat you will find it easier to rely on smaller game to stock your larder.

Because all wild meats can carry parasites harmful to man, they must be cooked thoroughly before consumption, regardless of how you preserve them. Efficient cooking destroys parasites and is therefore an essential part of field hygiene.

Drying

Drying or 'jerking' is the easiest way to preserve meat under survival conditions. First slice the meat into strips, approximately two inches wide and a quarter of an inch thick. Then string them on a thin stick or drape them over a bar on your drying rack. Make sure they are not touching each other.

Until the surface of the meat has dried you run the risk of flies laying their eggs in it. You can prevent this with two simple precautions. Either site your drying rack in a sunny and windy location or, the more effective method, lay a slow smouldering fire under the rack. This will speed up the drying process as well as keeping off insects. Make absolutely certain, however, that the fire is giving out only a low heat and not much smoke. Don't

Making a survival saus...

Dried meat can be made into pemmican – the survivor's sausage – by drying pieces of meat, mixing with berries and sealing with rendered fat.

use green vegetation to produce the smoke, or you will taint the meat. If you need to increase the smoke, use some damp wood chips or bark from a non-poisonous tree.

The smoking can be stopped once the surface of the meat is dry. Allow the meat to hang in the sun or a dry place until it is brittle. It can then be stored, wrapped in dry grass and bark, until you need it. To use dried meat, you can rehydrate it for broiling or steaming or, better still, just add it to a stew.

Pemmican

Once you have a store of dried meat, you can consider making pemmican, the survivors' home-made, high-energy, high-protein emergency ration. Pemmican is ideal for long hunting trips or if you intend to make a break from civilisation. Take your brittle dried meat and pound it between two rocks until it is a powder. You now have the equivalent of a survival stock cube. Next, mix the powdered meat with sun-dried berries and plenty of rendered fat. Form the resulting sticky mass into palm-sized pellets and place these in the cleaned large intestine of an animal. Seal the ends by tying and with fat. You now have a survival sausage which can be eaten as it is, or sliced and added to stews, or fried on a hot stone.

Freezing

In Arctic conditions you may be able to store your meat by letting it freeze. But remember – even when frozen, the scent of the meat will be detected by other hungry predators. Make certain it is out of their reach.

Be sure that you will be able to cope with the meat once it is frozen. The most common mistake made by survi-

vors is to freeze large pieces of meat. Instead, butcher it into meal size portions – they don't take a week to defrost. Make quite sure the meat is thoroughly defrosted before cooking.

Preserving fish

Your fish can be preserved along with your meat. Treat fish in the same way as meat – dry it, or make it into pemmican. The only difference is that fish goes off far more quickly, so must be dried as fast as possible. In all but the sunniest weather, this will mean you have to use a smudge fire or a smoke house.

Smoking

You can also deliberately flavour fish by smoking it. To do this you will need to hang the fish in a smoke house. Score the flesh before hanging, so that the smoke permeates the flesh better.

Smoking fish in a smoke house is little different to operating a smudge fire. A slow trickle of woodsmoke does the trick. Once you have started smoking the fish, check it on a regular

Drying fish in close-up: because fish goes off so quickly you must use a smudge fire or actually smoke the fish in a slow trickle of woodsmoke. Properly-smoked fish is one of the true delicacies available to the switched-on survivor.

basis. There are two stages in smoking fish: half smoking, and full smoking. Half-smoked fish is still soft and flavoured of wood, ready for eating. Fully smoked fish is dry and brittle. Treat it in the same way as dried meat.

Fish pemmican is certainly an acquired taste when eaten raw. But it is an excellent addition to soups and stews, and can be fried to make delicious fish cakes.

Preserving fungi

If you are lucky you may be stranded during a glut of edible fungi. To preserve them for future use, you can dry them.

First clean each individual fungus, cutting out any parts attacked by insects. Be particularly thorough with fungi that have gills or pores, as these are a favourite breeding ground for grubs. Then string the fungi together on a cord or stick, and hang them in your smoke house or shelter to dry. Some fungi such as the Horn of Plenty can be powdered to use as a stew flavouring, while others are best served whole as chewy stew ingredients.

Preserving plants

In general, plant foods are best used fresh. But at the onset of winter you must certainly consider stockpiling your supplies.

The easiest parts of plants to preserve are the young green leaves used for teas. Don't pick the leaves and store them in containers – simply dry the stalks of the plant itself. With plants such as nettles, use the fibres in the dried stem for cordage. Store bundles of useful herbs in your shelter or smoke house.

Heat the fat in a mess tin or similar to render it down and provide the liquefied fat which will bind the powdered meat into a stodgy mass. You can add dried berries for extra flavour.

The finished pemmican: the rendered fat and powdered meat mixture is stuffed into the cleaned-out intestine of a large animal. You can eat it cold, cutting off slices as you need them; or you can fry it or add it to stews.

Survival

Dry and grind up roots to use as flour, or bury them in layers of dry sand. Cover this to keep it dry.

Nuts are best stored either as a flour, or in open containers, still in their shells. Keep them dry and stir them regularly to prevent mildew.

Dry fruits by laying them on warm stones in the sun, and store them in containers with lids. Above all keep them dry.

The best way to store seeds long-term is by parching them. Only make flour in small batches. Otherwise you risk losing your whole crop to weevils.

Storing food

Your food store must be safe from mammals, must be dry, and must have a constant temperature. A properly constructed smoke house will meet many of these criteria, but don't use it to store all your food. "Never keep all your eggs in one basket" is the golden rule when storing your life-saving food.

The easiest larder to make is an underground cache. Try to find a dry, sheltered piece of ground – for example, under an overhanging bush or log. Dig a hole about two feet deep, and line the pit with bark slabs. Birch or cherry bark is ideal for this. Further line the pit with dried and, if possible, smoked grass. Place your food packages into the pit, followed by more grass. Then add some dried aromatic herb (such as marjoram) to disguise any scent from the food. Finally, seal the pit with bark and the soil you originally removed.

Take care to note exactly where you have buried the food, or mark the location so that you can find it again even after a heavy snowfall.

Predator, thief, and carrion crow!

No animal will stop itself stealing your food out of a sense of fair play. In the same way, don't miss any opportunity to steal from a wild animal. You can turn even the rotting remains of a predator's meal into a life-saving stew if you are hungry enough. Skin and gut the remains in the normal way, and then thoroughly boil the rancid meat for as long as possible. To eat the stew you will need to hold your nose, but it will keep you alive.

This emergency stew *cannot* be reheated. Discard what you don't eat. If you reheat it, a dangerous botulism results.

Hanging food
You can preserve food from the attentions of the local wildlife by numerous methods. A tall sapling can be bent back and game secured to it, which will keep it out of reach while you are away from the camp.

Rope bundle
Another method of ke[...] food out of reach is to [...] it between two trees, [...] like a hammock.

Two can play this game
Animals may try to make off with your food, but you can do the same to them. Even rotten meat from an old kill can be eaten if you boil it a long time and hold your nose when eating it. It may be disgusting, but it could save your life.

Bark breaks
If you are going to store [...] of food out of reach of animals on a regular basis [...] you will need to stop squirrels and other small mammals from climbing [...] A metal sheet fixed round [...] the trunk will prevent the[...] from being able to grip.

Drying meat
To prepare meat for drying or smoking, cut it into strip[...] along the grain of the mea[...] The strips should be about [...] five cm wide and just und[...] a centimetre thick.

Keith Fretwell

Here two grizzled survivors are preserving enough food to see them through a Canadian winter, but their larder is being raided. One of the problems with preserved food is that it attracts the attention of all sorts of animal life, from the weevil to the brown bear. The problem does not disappear with the onset of winter: even frozen food in the Arctic can be sniffed out by the enterprising polar bear, and unless you are well armed you can't argue with him.

Smoking meat

Smoke your meat over a wood fire using timber from a deciduous tree, ideally willow or birch. Do not use conifers like pine or fir trees because their smoke will impart a vile taste to the meat. You can hang meat high above a slow, smouldering fire, but a quicker method is to dig a hole about a metre deep and 50 cm wide. Get a fire going at the bottom and pile on green wood to create the smoke. Place the meat on an improvised grate over the hole. One night of heavy smoking will preserve meat for five to seven days; two nights and it will remain edible for two to four weeks. When properly smoked, the meat will look like a dark, curled stick. It is highly nutritious and, best of all, it tastes good.

Wind curing
You can cure meat by hanging it up to let the sun and wind do the job of a smudge fire. Try to hang it at least five metres high so that the flies cannot get to it.

.44 Magnum
In the USA some people pack a .44 when they go hunting just in case they have a problem with their rifle when they encounter something particularly beefy. This may sound extreme, but it could be disagreeable to find yourself nose to nose with a grizzly and nothing but a .22 survival rifle in your hand.

Fire reflector
These survivors have built a simple reflector from logs which enables them to gain the maximum benefit from their fire.

Fat and soap
A useful by-product of pemmican-making is soap. If you have any rendered fat left over, mix two parts fat with one part of wood ash from the fire. Boil it until it thickens and you have a primitive but effective form of soap. Not quite Imperial Leather, but it will do.

Fighting Fit

What it takes to be a Combat Infantryman

FIRST BATTLE CAMP

Above: Use your left hand to pull the butt backwards and downwards, keeping your left elbow as far forward as is comfortable.

The Light Infantry

The Royal Green Jackets

Right: Alternatively you can hold the butt with your left hand underneath the butt.

Left: The Close Quarter Battle firing posit. Step forward with your left leg in the direc of the target, keep your body leaning forw and press the GPMG into your right side. ? by sense of direction and correct your sho by observing the strike of each burst.

Keep your heels flat on the ground and move your body right up to the GPMG so your shoulder is firmly pressed against the butt. You can test if your firing position is good by rocking back and forth: the foresight should move up and down on the point of aim.

By week 11 of your training you're half-way to becoming a fully-fledged combat infantryman: you've passed off the square, you're fitter than you've ever been, and you've learned to handle and live-fire the SA80 and the LSW. Your coveted green beret is the mark of your growing professionalism. Now comes your first battle camp, and at last you can put into practice everything you've learned so far.

This week marks a turning point for those who are over 18. By the end of it, you'll know enough about real soldiering to know whether you want to make it your life for the next few years. If you don't, you've until the end of week 12 to opt out. Some do – but most decide to face the challenge.

First battle camp is certainly a challenge. You travel up to a large training area in the hills of south Wales, and you live out for a week. You set up a patrol base camp and learn to live in it for a protracted period. You mount patrols from the base camp by night: first, a reconnaissance patrol, then – when you have located the enemy – a fighting patrol.

'Terrorist contact'

The next day, you occupy an observation post (OP) overlooking a deserted Welsh farmhouse on the training area. While you are watching through your binoculars you suddenly see the 'terrorist' leader you have been after all week meet some of his devotees in front of the farm. Your heart jumps – you're so involved that for a moment you think you're reporting a real terrorist contact. You grab your radio and report back to platoon HQ exactly what is unfolding in front of you. Clearly the farmhouse is a meeting place.

Firing the GPMG

The famous GPMG will be retained by the British Army despite the introduction of the LSW. It will no longer be carried by dismounted infantrymen as a section weapon, but it will be fitted to virtually all armoured vehicles and to as many 'soft skinned' vehicles (lorries and Land Rovers) as possible, giving them some sort of self-protection ability.

The GPMG will also be retained in its Sustained Fire (SF) role. In this configuration, the butt is removed and it is mounted on a tripod and provided with a Dial Sight that allows targets to be registered and recorded. Thus, by dialling up certain co-ordinates, targets can be engaged blind in the dark or in bad visibility. Thus certain infantrymen are still trained in the use of the GPMG, some of them during their basic training.

The GPMG is 1.231 metres long, weighs 10.9 kg, is gas and spring operated and belt fed, has a cyclic rate of fire of 750 to at least 900 rounds per minute, and a sight range of 200 to 1800 metres. In its SF role the weight of the gun, including tripod, is 13.62 kg.

The GPMG is an automatic weapon and so is most effective when fired in bursts. You need to fire three to five rounds at longer ranges to observe the strike of shots and to correct errors in range and wind allowance. One round in four is tracer, to help with this. The length of the burst, however, is determined by the type of target, its range and your skill. A burst of eight to 10 rounds spreads more, but gives a better chance of hitting a moving target and may be necessary at very short ranges against a mass attack.

The longer burst can be also extremely effective when firing at the front of an enemy armoured vehicle, particularly if aimed at devices that assist crew vision when the vehicle is closed down – such as periscopes, image intensification or infra-red equipment, or even headlights or spotlights.

Rapid fire is the fastest rate at which you can maintain your accuracy, and should only be used when absolutely necessary – such as when there are a large number of enemy infantry in the open at short range or when providing covering fire for an attack by your own troops.

Whenever possible normal rates of fire should be used – short bursts of 2-3 rounds – mainly because the gun is easier to control and much more accurate, but also because sustained rapid fire will overheat the barrel. This quickly wears it out and affects its accuracy.

If possible, during a lull in the fighting, you should unload the gun, cock the action and raise the top cover so that the gun can cool down after sustained rapid fire. Each gun team carries a spare barrel and this should be changed after every 400 rounds, and not used again until it is cool to the touch. Apart from anything else, ammunition is always short and resupply may be difficult.

Carrying the gun, using the carrying handle. If there is a long distance to be covered, on the command 'Prepare to move' make the gun safe and fold the loaded belt over the GPMG.

1 Tilt the gun to the right, open the top cover and position the belt on the feed tray. Hold the belt in place with your left hand and close the top cover.

2 Set the sights, then cock the gun with your right hand, still holding the butt up with your left.

3 Press the trigger just long enough to fire two or three rounds. Longer bursts are only needed at long range, moving targets or mass attacks.

4 As soon as you release the trigger, observe where strike lands so you can correct your aim if you misjudged the range or wind allowance.

By carrying the GPMG like this you make it harder for the enemy to see that you are armed with a machine-gun and are therefore a prime target.

Fighting Fit

As a result of your report, the platoon commander decides to mount an area ambush of the farmhouse the following night. After you've planned and rehearsed the ambush, the operation goes ahead.

Enemy sighted

You've been there several hours, struggling to keep awake, when suddenly an urgent tug on the communication cord by the cut-off group warns you that the enemy has been sighted. You wait until the platoon commander tells you to pull the cord to illuminate the trip flare – then all hell breaks loose as LSWs and SA80s open up. Most of the enemy are 'killed', others make a run for it and are engaged by the cut-off groups. Okay, it was rigged – but it seemed very real!

Into the air

You practise anti-ambush drills on foot and in vehicles, you go through the section battle drills for an entire day, and you complete several forced marches.

Usually the platoon commander manages to get hold of an Army Air Corps, RAF or RN helicopter for a day. When the chopper arrives you're briefed on embussing and debussing drills, emergency procedures, where to sit, and so on. Everyone gets a ride, usually flying fast and low, keeping to the contours of the hills. If you've not flown in a helicopter before it's a fantastic experience. If he can, the platoon commander will fit the helicopter into the exercise, so your ride does have some tactical meaning.

At the end of the week you're exhausted. You feel you could sleep for 24 hours. You've been wet, cold, and very, very tired. But you've hacked it!

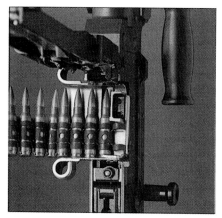

Detail of the feed tray: note that the links are uppermost and the leading round rests against the cartridge stop. Always check the links are not damaged before loading a belt.

Sustained fire role

Above and below: The GPMG mounted on a tripod for the Sustained Fire (SF) role. Its flat trajectory means that it can lay down a belt of fire up to 600 metres long, no bullet reaching more than 60 cm from the ground.

The GPMG continues to provide valuable support for the infantryman in combat.

Each infantry company has three GPMG (SF) conversion kits consisting of tripod and dial sight. The crews of these additional GPMGs are normally drawn from the bugle or drum platoon in an infantry battalion, but this varies in different regiments. GPMGs in the light role mounted on vehicles are manned by either the vehicle commander or possibly even one of soldiers in the back of a lorry, which is why it is important that as many infantrymen as possible should still be familiar with the GPMG despite its replacement by the LSW in a rifle section.

The GPMG needs to be balanced to find the best gas regulator setting to ensure reliability combined with minimum vibration. The setting should push the working parts sufficiently far back to result in automatic fire, but not so far back as to cause accentuated wear and unnecessary vibration. This is a matter of trial and error.

When the gun is balanced you will then learn to group with the GPMG so that you can produce a 500-mm group of 20 rounds at 100-metres range. As with the SA80 and LSW, you must then zero the weapon from the 100-metre firing point by firing four five-round belts. When the weapon is zeroed to you, the next stage is for you to fire progressive practices at 200,300 and 400 metres. When you are competent at these ranges you will learn to engage targets at 500 and 600 metres.

Remember that the GPMG, unless you are firing it in the SF role using a dial sight, has only a conventional iron sight, so at 500 and 600 metres it is extremely difficult to observe the strike of your rounds. This is where the gun controller comes into his own using his binoculars and correcting the fall of shot.

Combat Report

Vietnam:
Combat Air Controller

George Perkins was an enlisted Combat Air Controller in the US Air Force during the early days of the Vietnam war.

From the time "advisers" first went to Vietnam in 1961 until the American withdrawal in 1973, a small band of US air force men had the difficult task of directing close air support. The airmen spent much of their time on the ground and faced as much danger as infantrymen.

In those days, they didn't have time for fancy training to make you a Combat Air Controller. They just stuck you in the bushes, slung a radio over your back, and told you to do the job.

The job, of course, involved directing aircraft in attacks against ground targets. Up to that time, it had always been customary for the Air Force to have its own men on the ground – right there with the foot-slogging GIs – to direct close air support.

In 1961, I was one of three dozen NCOs selected to become Air Commandos, our service's answer to the Green Berets – another 'elite' unit personally backed by President Kennedy. In the tidal marshlands at Eglin Air Force Base near Fort Walton Beach on the west Florida coast, we were training for a war most Americans hadn't heard about yet.

I stepped off a C-124 at Saigon's Tan Son Nhut Airport on 21 October 1962, along with a dozen other guys from the original Air Commando contingent. We wore ANZAC campaign headgear – Australian hats with turned-up brims which were to become the Air Commando symbol.

A gung-ho Green Beret

We were a close-knit group. The day of my arrival, the guys were talking about how the Viet Cong had shot down one of our number, Major Al Saunders. Luckily, he'd been rescued under heavy fire. Al had been piloting a T-28, the primitive fighter-bomber we were teaching the Vietnamese to fly.

I was sent down to the Delta, to a Special Forces "B" Camp run by 34-year-old Major Ernest Trevor from Columbus, Georgia. Trevor was a gung-ho Green Beret. He liked us Air Force guys but doubted we'd be much use to him. He was wrong.

On 1 November 1962, South Vietnamese troopers under Trevor's tutelage were ambushed by a surprisingly heavy Viet Cong force. They were pinned down in a deserted hamlet by withering fire from a high, thickly-vegetated slope.

A South Vietnamese T-28 drops napalm onto Viet Cong positions. Napalm was not as effective as its spectacular bursts led the Air Force to believe.

Men were getting killed all around us. Mortar shells careened into our midst, coughing up clods of earth and spraying shrapnel. Bursts of automatic gunfire whipped over my head as I snake-crawled toward the spot where Major Trevor and Captain Andy Stockwell were assessing the situation.

I got on the radio. A flight of T-28s was in the area, ready to help out.

"Do your stuff," Stockwell urged, a little sarcastically. "Get those 28s in here and plaster the Cong."

"That's what I'm here for, sir. But it isn't that simple."

"Huh?"

"We have to pinpoint the VC. All I see is muzzle flashes."

We walked into three Cong

I got on the radio and confirmed with the T-28 flight leader that he was carrying napalm and rockets. He was using the callsign "Straight Flush", and I recognised the voice of Captain John R. Watkins, the 'wild man' of our Air Commando outfit. Watkins was supposedly 'advising' the South Vietnamese who piloted the three other T-28s, but that was sheer fiction. He was in command.

I learned that Watkins had sufficient fuel. I instructed him to wait a mile south of the battle zone. I rounded up two of Trevor's Vietnamese troops and we began hacking our way uphill from the hamlet, slicing through the brush with machetes. It was sheer hell, lugging that PRC-10 radio and a Colt-Armalite rifle – the weapon developed by the Air Force which would later become the standard M16.

Then we literally walked into three stray Cong. They were spindly little men in black garb, lugging carbines. Less than three metres apart, we exchanged gunfire. I killed two, one of my men got the third. My other man, Corporal Diem, was hit in the shoulder and thigh and was bleeding profusely.

"Damn!" I thought aloud. "We've got to get closer."

I assured Diem we'd be back. With Sergeant Tranh, I kept going uphill through heavy brush. The muzzle flashes from VC weapons were closer now.

Suddenly, the radio crackled. "This is Straight Flush. How are you doing down there?"

Captain Watkins' words carried to the VC above us. Suddenly, they were shooting at us. Tranh and I hit the deck as grenades began exploding in the heavy foliage nearby. But we'd seen enough: a row of men hunched over their guns behind a straight barrier of sandbags on the ridge crest. There were at least 100 of them, far more than we'd thought.

A grenade ripped off branches above my head. Shrapnel tore through my fatigues, slashing my arms, back, buttocks. Tranh was cut up even worse. I clutched the radio desperately and cried out:

"Straight Flush, this is Amber Rose. Make a low firing pass from the south west, over the village. Hit the slope three-quarters of the way up and give your bombs a 100-yard spread."

Watkins couldn't believe it. "Won't we be hitting you?"

"You'll be close. But if you don't do it quick, we'll be cut to pieces up here."

I heard the sharp whine of their engines as the T-28s dived and levelled off over the hamlet. Then the aircraft were roaring over our heads and silvery napalm bombs tumbled from their wings. The T-28s pulled away, leaving a fire storm sweeping over the ridge crest.

Almost as an afterthought, one of the tiny fighter-bombers began spewing smoke. VC small-arms fire had riddled its fuselage. The plane wobbled, fell, and exploded against a hillside.

Something bothered me

Minutes later, it was all over. I came out, only mildly hurt, with Tranh and Diem. Trevor's men found 65 burnt corpses on the ridge crest – all Viet Cong. We had scored what the South Vietnamese would later call a "great victory", but to me it was all a little sickening.

I stayed with the Green Berets in the Delta for four months. Most of it was a repeat of my first experience. To pinpoint targets for the T-28s and A-1 Skyraiders, I constantly had to take greater risks than the ground troops I was supporting. Often, our radio communications were garbled. When I was talking to Vietnamese pilots, they hardly seemed to understand at all. Once, another Combat Air Controller had such poor contact with a Vietnamese flier that he caused napalm to be dropped on his own men. There were 26 casualties.

Something else bothered me, too. It was the impersonal aspect of our pilots swooping down from the sky to drop napalm on human beings. Napalm is burning gasoline, treated with a chemical that causes it to cling to human skin. Often the corpses were blackened, bloated. Later in the war, the Combat Air Controller's job was abolished and the function was taken over by pilots flying Bird Dog observation planes – but they never got to see the results of bombing the way we did. It was horrible.

A Viet Cong soldier lies in a twisted heap after a napalm strike. The Combat Air Controller could often seen the dreadful result of a strike.

THE BUNKER BUSTER 66-mm LAW

The Light Infantry

The Royal Green Jackets

1 To fire a LAW, remove the rear cover retaining pin, grasp the rear cover at the top and pull it down. This frees the front and rear cover and the sling assembly.

2 Now extend the tube by pulling the rear sight cover until it locks into position.

Above: Aiming the 66mm LAW (Light Anti-Tank Weapon), a self contained unit which consists of a rocket packed into an expendable launcher-container. It is a valuable addition to your section's firepower, useful against light armoured vehicles and bunkers.

You're back from a well-earned long weekend's leave after first battle camp in Week 11 — and you've still a lot to learn before enduring the rigours of final battle camp. So, for the next four weeks, you're in barracks almost all the time, soaking up information and improving your skills, on the 'consolidation' course.

In many ways life is more straightforward from Week 12, because you've got rid of those few recruits whose hearts weren't really in it. Now it's just those of you who want to make it and, because you're all aiming for the same thing, you help each other. The feeling of team spirit and loyalty to each other grows all the time. When you've been through so much together you feel a strong bond.

This is what the infantry and the Regimental system is all about. Very few men are *really* prepared to die for their country, but they are, if necessary, prepared to die for their mates. It's during this time that you really start to identify with and feel part of the Regiment.

The Personal Weapon Test

But there's still so much more to learn. You're reasonably expert on the SA80 and LSW, and you're started on the 66-mm LAW, the 84-mm MAW and the grenade. Now, you consolidate your knowledge on all these weapons. You have to be good enough to fire them all in field firing conditions in Wales on final battle camp in week 17.

But before you do any field firing you have to pass your Annual Personal Weapon Test (APWT) on the range. This is fired under test conditions and, as an infantryman, you *have* to pass. If you do well, you are classified as a marksman and qualify

If the round lands short of the enemy tank you have judged the lead correctly but misjudged the range.

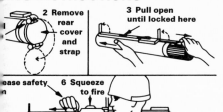

2 Remove rear cover and strap

3 Pull open until locked here

?ease safety ?n   6 Squeeze to fire

Firing the LAW

The Rocket 66-mm, HEAT, LIAI is a complete weapon system consisting of a lightweight, shoulder-fired launcher and HEAT rocket, originally developed in the US. The weapon is issued as a pre-loaded, single-shot, disposable launcher that can be fired from any one of the normal firing positions, and provides the section with a rugged, reliable and lightweight anti-tank weapon.

The weapon system weighs 2.2 kg and is 878 mm long when fully extended. The launcher tube serves as a protective package for the rocket, and requires no maintenance. The weapon is prepared for firing easily and quickly and is extremely accurate, giving good results on all targets up to a maximum effective range of 200 metres although the sight is graduated up to 350 metres. No zeroing is necessary.

The rocket is capable of penetrating 275 mm of armour and is extremely effective, as was demonstrated in the Falklands War, against bunkers, machine-gun emplacements and other fortified targets. When the rocket is fired there is a backblast danger area that must be clear of any troops, equipment or obstruction. This area extends rearward from the launcher for 40 metres at an angle of 310 mils on each side of the line of fire.

You prepare the 66-mm for firing by removing the front and rear covers, then, grasping the backsight housing with one hand and holding the outer tube with the other, you pull sharply outwards, which brings the weapon to the extended position ready for firing. The mechanism is now cocked.

The sights are very simple. Both the backsight and foresight are spring-loaded so that they spring up when the launcher tubes are extended. On the backsight is a large aperture at the top; this is used in conjunction with the small tip on the foresight, which has a luminous spot. These are the battle sights for use at night or in bad visibility and for quick aimed shots at targets up to 100 metres away.

The two smaller apertures on the backsight are marked either +°C or –°C and are used in conjunction with the rest of the foresight according to the temperature conditions. For temperatures above freezing the lower aperture is used; for temperatures below freezing the upper one is used. The foresight is made of clear plastic. Ranges are represented by the horizontal lines. The vertical central line is the aiming line to be used for a stationary, receding or approaching target. The outside vertical lines represent the amount of aim off required to hit a 15 mph crossing target.

When you fully understand the sighting system, which is fairly rudimentary and designed to deal with close targets in emergency situations, you need to practise the firing procedure. Having prepared the weapon for firing, you first check that the backblast danger area is clear and that the sights are set at the appropriate temperature setting. You then place the weapon on your shoulder so that your forehead is against the backsight. With your right hand, pull forward the safety catch to the 'Arm' position. Put your fingers on the trigger and thumb underneath the tube when the

3 Pull the safety forward to the 'arm' position. The LAW is now ready to fire.

The front sight blade is made of transparent plastic with a reticle stamped on it. It pops up into position when you pull the launcher open.

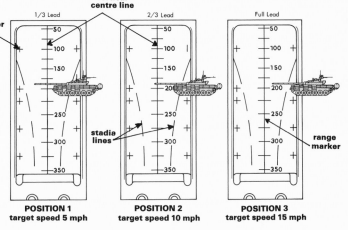

vertical centre line

lead marker

1/3 Lead

2/3 Lead

Full Lead

stadia lines

range marker

POSITION 1
target speed 5 mph

POSITION 2
target speed 10 mph

POSITION 3
target speed 15 mph

The centre line of the sight is graded in metres: the curved stadia lines on either side help you estimate range. To shoot a moving target use the crosses on the side of the sight to judge the lead: a vehicle moving at 15 mph needs full lead, one travelling at 5 mph needs only a third lead.

Fire another LAW at the same target, applying the necessary correction, and you should obtain a hit.

Because of LAW's relative inaccuracy it is a good idea to fire volleys of them at individual targets to guarantee a hit and improve the chance of a kill. This is quicker and safer than firing single shots and applying corrections if they miss.

Once you have looked behind you to see no-one is in the backblast area and acquired your sight picture, gently press down the rubber-covered trigger. This goes down a long way before it fires.

to wear special insignia, the Crossed Rifles, on your sleeve.

At this stage, you start to concentrate on defence – how to occupy a defensive position, routine in defence, the dimensions of a slit trench and how to dig and conceal it.

Meet the musclebusters

On top of all this, you continue relentlessly with the gruelling PT sessions, the swimming, the road runs and the assault course sessions. The people in charge of you for all these physical activities are the musclemen of the Army Physical Training Corps (APTC).

The 'musclebusters', as they are called, are as wide as they are tall, and can quite happily do 'press-ups' or 'push-ups' all day long if necessary. The trouble is they expect you to be able to, as well! But they're highly professional – building you up gradually but persistently, until by week 15 they have transformed you. Sometimes you hate their guts but they are good – you've got to give it to them – and in the end you're grateful to them.

The last test

The highlight of the consolidation course is the March and Shoot – if highlight is the right word. This is a six-mile march (though you run most of the way), in full combat order with rifle, and wearing your tin helmet. Each section in the platoon competes for the best time, and so you go flat out.

Your destination is the range, where you complete a demanding assault course and then fire 10 rounds at targets 200 metres away. The idea is to see if you're ready for battle (simulated by the assault course and the shooting) after a long march. This is a hard test, but by this stage you're fit enough to hack it.

So, by the end of week 15, you're ready for the climax of your training as a combat infantryman – three weeks at final battle camp in Wales!

Make safe!

Top view of the 66 mm LAW: here the safety has been pulled out and the rocket is armed and ready to fire.

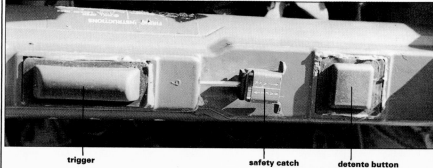

trigger   safety catch   detente button

If you have cocked the 66 mm but decide not to fire, depress the detente button, which re-engages the safety catch and 'unlocks' the tube.

Collapse the tube, then replace the front and rear covers and the sling assembly.

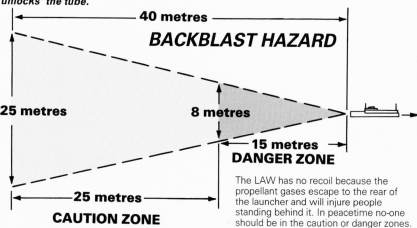

40 metres

BACKBLAST HAZARD

25 metres

8 metres

15 metres
DANGER ZONE

25 metres
CAUTION ZONE

The LAW has no recoil because the propellant gases escape to the rear of the launcher and will injure people standing behind it. In peacetime no-one should be in the caution or danger zones.

correct aim has been taken, restrain your breathing so as not to disturb the aim, and push down on the trigger with all four fingers. When you have fired, try to observe the strike of the round so that you can make any necessary corrections for subsequent rockets fired. When you have done this, the launcher tube may be discarded.

The 66-mm LAW is a section weapon and any man in the section should be capable of firing it. When siting the weapon in a defensive position, a field of fire of up to 200 metres is required so that you take advantage of the rocket's maximum range. Careful concealment is vital, since it will be necessary to allow a target to approach your position in order to ensure a first-round kill. Site the weapon so as to cover likely tank approaches such as gaps in minefields or firm and open ground.

If possible, the 66-mm should be sited in a defilade position, hiding the backblast from any enemy observing your positions. Also, bearing in mind the relatively limited penetrative ability of

the 66-mm, you should aim to engage the sides or rear of enemy tanks. The best firing position is from a fire trench, though you should ensure that not more than one man armed with the 66-mm is in any one trench. His companion should be a rifleman.

The 66-mm is particularly suitable for tank hunting or stalking because it is light and small and can easily be carried on a night patrol whose mission is to destroy enemy tanks in a static position and from close range. It is much more difficult to 'bug out' in a hurry after a night attack against enemy tanks if you are carrying a bulky and heavy 84-mm. Once you have fired your 66-mm, on the other hand, you are free to defend yourself using your SA80.

The 66-mm LAW is a simple and effective one-shot anti-tank weapon. Firing and aiming techniques are quickly assimilated. Although of limited penetrative capability, it can disable or destroy a tank if it hits a vulnerable point. It provides an excellent last-ditch capability for the infantryman.